Exercises in

Physical Geology

Fifth Edition

W. K. Hamblin
Brigham Young University
Provo, Utah

J. D. Howard
Skidaway Institute of Oceanography
Savannah, Georgia

Burgess Publishing Company
Minneapolis, Minnesota

Editorial: Wayne Schotanus, Marta Reynolds
Copy editing: Elisabeth Sovik
Production: Morris Lundin
Design: Dennis Tasa

Burgess Publishing Company
7108 Ohms Lane
Minneapolis, Minnesota 55435

20   19   18   17   16   15   14   13   12   11

Preface

Exercises in Physical Geology is now in its fifth edition and fifteenth year of publication. In this new edition we present updated exercise material to keep pace with the new concepts that are rapidly developing in the geological sciences. Nearly every exercise has been revised to improve its clarity and usefulness. In some instances this has required a new approach with new materials and in others a simple update of methods and procedures used in earlier editions.

Rocks and Minerals

The photographs of rocks and minerals are the same as those used in the fourth edition and are intended as reference material for comparison with laboratory specimens. Although photographs cannot replace actual hand specimens, they are useful as a study guide and reference. Special attention is given to illustrations of rock textures because texture is one of the most important keys to the identification and interpretation of rocks.

Topographic Maps and Aerial Photographs

The second section of the manual is a series of exercises on the interpretation of landforms as expressed on topographic maps and aerial photographs. Each exercise includes a statement of objectives, main concepts, and supporting ideas, as well as improved block diagrams illustrating geologic processes. Three types of material are provided in each exercise: (1) an aerial photograph, (2) a series of topographic maps, and (3) sets of stereo aerial photographs at the back of the book, which can be removed from the manual and used as contact prints in a manner similar to that used in professional geologic work.

Structural Geology

The section on structural geology has been considerably revised with the use of full-color diagrams and maps. A new series of diagrams illustrating basic structural features has been included as a ready reference to the geometry of folds and faults.

We have also used full color in the series of block diagrams illustrating the basic outcrop pattern shown on geologic maps, and the color on the block diagrams is keyed to the standard colors used on the U.S. Geological Survey Maps (i.e., older rocks are shown in blue, purple, and gray hues similar to those used to illustrate Paleozoic rocks, and younger strata are shown in shades of green and yellow like those used to illustrate Mesozoic and Cenozoic rocks). This should make students familiar with the standard color scheme used on geologic maps and help them to really see the basic age relationships of the major rock bodies.

In the structure section we have retained the portions of the geologic map of the United States used in previous editions, but have added new maps of the Grand Canyon and the Appalachian Mountains.

Plate Tectonics

The theory of plate tectonics has influenced every aspect of geology; hence, it is integrated into most of the exercises in this manual. It is given particular emphasis in the exercises on the tectonics of North America and on the geology of the ocean floor. As a basic reference we have included a new tectonic map of North America, simplified and redrafted from the U.S. Geological Survey map by P. King. We have also included new full-color physiographic maps of the ocean floor which illustrate subtle details of the submarine landscape. The exercises on plate tectonics and on the topography of the ocean floor are designed to help students understand many of the regional features of the earth and some of the factual information upon which the theory of plate tectonics is based.

Planetary Geology

Planetary geology adds an exciting new dimension to the study of the earth because it permits us to compare and contrast the geology of the earth with that of other planets of the solar system. We have updated this section to include recent developments in studies of the inner planets and the exciting exploration of the moons of Jupiter.

Environmental Geology

The section on environmental geology has been modified by the addition of new maps and photos and by a revised discussion of principles and problems. Some questions of environmental geology have been integrated into each exercise where appropriate, but the major study of the geologic environment is in Exercise 20.

Objectives

In spite of the changes and modifications that improve and update the fifth edition, the objectives set forth in the second edition still stand:

1. To give students experience in examining geologic data and formulating hypotheses to explain observed facts.
2. To give students an opportunity to continue laboratory-type work outside of class so they can prepare adequately for lab sessions and review work independently after lab sessions.
3. To give laboratory instructors maximum latitude in their instruction by providing abundant material which they can adapt to their own specific objectives.

January 1980

W.K.H.
J.D.H.

Acknowledgments

We are grateful for the constructive criticism received from the many laboratory instructors who have used this manual in past years. We have tried to incorporate their valuable comments into this revision, and we hope they will continue to provide suggestions for improvement.

We sincerely thank Dennis Tasa, of Tasa Graphic Arts, who prepared numerous text illustrations, and Elisabeth Sovik, who copy edited the text.

The U.S. Geological Survey topographic maps, which appear in blue, brown, and black in this book, are faithful reproductions of U.S. Geological Survey maps originally published in several colors. These maps are designed for teaching purposes only and are not intended to duplicate the complete maps. We are grateful to the U.S. Geological Survey for permission to reproduce these topographic maps, sections of geologic maps, and aerial photographs.

We also thank the Agricultural Stabilization and Conservation Services of the U.S. Department of Agriculture for the use of aerial photographs from their files, and the Surveys and Mapping Branch of the Department of Energy, Mines, and Resources of Canada for permission to publish the aerial photographs that appear on pages 120, 121, 128, 206, and 207 and the geologic map of Mount Eisenhower on page 159. Dr. Bruce Molnia of the U.S. Geological Survey kindly furnished the air photos of Icy Bay, Alaska, which appear on page 117.

Contents

To the Student

Exercises in Physical Geology is not simply a manual but is a series of studies employing topographic maps, aerial photographs, geologic maps, and seismic profiler records. An important innovation is the utilization of stereo photographs reproduced to their actual size and included in a separate section at the back of the book. These photographs must be removed from the book and used with a stereoscope in the same way a professional geologist would use prints of stereo photographs in daily work and research.

1 Introduction to Minerals: Crystal Growth

A mineral is composed of elements or groups of elements which unite in nature to form an inorganic crystalline solid. Every crystalline substance has a definite internal structure in which the atoms occur in specific proportions and are arranged in an orderly geometric pattern. This systematic arrangement of atoms is one of the most significant aspects of a mineral. It exists throughout the entire specimen, and, if crystallization occurs under ideal conditions, it will be expressed in perfect crystal faces. Moisture in the air, for example, may freeze and develop into crystals of ice. The form of the solid ice crystals is an external expression of the orderly arrangement of the hydrogen and oxygen atoms. Although each individual crystal is different in size and shape, all possess the same properties of symmetry. Similarly, a solution rich in sodium (Na) and chlorine (Cl) will, upon evaporation, develop crystals of halite (NaCl), or common salt. A model of the atomic framework of halite is shown in Figure 1, and a sketch showing the resulting crystal form is shown in Figure 2. Minerals with poor or imperfect crystal faces, however, still possess a systematic internal structure, as is indicated by the symmetrical patterns produced from x-ray studies. In contrast, atoms in a liquid or gas have little or no systematic structure and no definite form. Substances which become solid without crystallizing are *amorphous*, i.e., without a definite internal structure. Glass, for example, is rigid and solid, but the atoms are not arranged in a systematic pattern, so many physicists regard glass as an extremely viscous liquid.

A very significant feature of crystals is the constancy of their interfacial angles. The angles between similar faces of a specific mineral will be the same, even though the size of the crystal may vary (Figure 3). This unique feature is of prime importance in differentiating minerals which are similar in other respects. Pyroxene and amphibole, very similar in chemical composition and physical appearance, may be readily differentiated by the fact that amphibole forms crystals with interfacial angles of 124 and 56 degrees, whereas pyroxene has interfacial angles of 87 and 93 degrees. Numerous, precise measurements of the angles between crystal faces have repeatedly demonstrated that although crystals of the same substance exhibit different overall shapes, *the angles between corresponding faces are identical*. This is known as the *law of constancy of interfacial angles*.

A much better understanding of the crystalline structure of minerals can be gained if one observes the process of crystal growth and summarizes his observations concerning the nature of crystals. The major objectives of this exercise are:

1. To observe crystal growth and distinguish a single crystal from an aggregate.
2. To study the law of constancy of interfacial angles by observing crystals growing from an aqueous solution.
3. To discover some of the factors governing crystal growth.

Growth of Crystals from a Melt

Most minerals originating from a melt (or magma) crystallize at temperatures well above the boiling point of water, so it is difficult to directly observe their crystal growth. Thymol, an organic chemical, however, crystallizes near room temperature and, although it is different from a magma, certain principles of crystallization demonstrated in a thymol melt pertain generally to a magma. Thymol is not poisonous but should be handled with forceps, for it may irritate the skin and eyes.

1

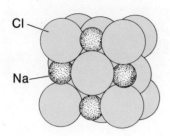

Figure 1. Diagram showing arrangement of Na and Cl atoms in halite.

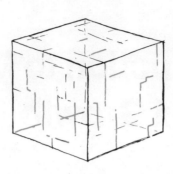

Figure 2. Crystal form of halite.

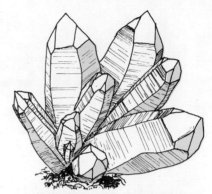

Figure 3. Cluster of quartz crystals illustrating constancy of interfacial angles. Although size and shape of the crystals vary, angles between adjacent crystal faces are constant.

Procedure

A. Slow cooling without "seed" crystals

Place a petri dish containing a small amount of crystalline thymol on a hot plate at low heat until all the crystals are melted. Let the melt continue to heat for one to two minutes and then set it aside to cool slowly where it will not be disturbed. *This melt will be examined near the end of the lab.*

B. Slow cooling with "seed" crystals

1. Repeat the procedure described above but transfer the petri dish to the stage of the microscope as soon as the thymol is melted. Add several (four or five) "seed" crystals to the melt and observe it under the microscope. As the melt cools, you will see the crystals begin to grow.

2. Briefly describe the manner of crystal growth. Consider such factors as internal expansion versus external accretion, rate of growth, direction of growth, angles between crystal faces, and the effect of limited space on crystal shape.
   a. How do the growth lines of a crystal compare with the outline of a single crystal in a solid aggregate?
   b. What role do the "seed" crystals play in initiating crystal growth?

3. When less than half of the melt remains, you may notice some spontaneously nucleating crystals forming. Study them as they grow. Make a sketch of the final crystalline aggregate in the space provided below. Individual crystals may be recognized by characteristic growth lines and reflection of light. The aggregate of crystals produced in this experiment is similar to that found in many common igneous rocks. Both are composed of many interlocking crystals originating from a melt. Examine several specimens of granite supplied by your instructor. Discriminate between the individual crystals and make a sketch of the texture of a granite. How does the aggregate of thymol compare with the granite?

Aggregate of Thymol Crystals   **Texture of a Granite**

C. Rapid cooling

Place a petri dish containing a small amount of thymol on a hot plate until only a few crystals remain. Transfer the dish to the top of an ice cube and let it cool for a fraction of a minute. As the melt cools rapidly you will see the crystals begin to grow, and almost immediately several independent spontaneously nucleating centers of crystallization develop. Quickly transfer the petri dish to the stage of a microscope and observe the nature of the crystal growth. Repeat the experiment as often as time permits so you may be sure of your general observations and conclusions.

D. Examine the thymol in the first dish prepared for Part A of this exercise. *What effect does the rate of cooling have on crystal size?*

Growth of Crystals from Solution

Many minerals are precipitated from aqueous solutions by evaporation at atmospheric temperature and pressure. Crystal growth of such minerals can thus be observed in the laboratory by evaporating prepared concentrated solutions.

Procedure

A. Your instructor will provide a concentrated solution of sodium chloride, sodium nitrate, potassium aluminum sulfate (alum), and copper acetate.

Place a drop of each solution on a slide. Label each solution on a piece of tape placed at the end of the slide. As the water evaporates, crystals of each compound will appear; as evaporation continues, the crystals will grow larger.

1. How does crystallization from an aqueous solution compare with crystallization from a melt?

2. Do the crystals of each compound fit the law of constancy of interfacial angles?

3. Does each compound have a unique crystal form?

4. Can minerals be identified from crystal form alone?

5. On the basis of this exercise, what is the relationship between cooling and grain size?

2 Physical Properties and Mineral Identification

Properties of Minerals

In addition to having an internal structure, a mineral has a definite chemical composition which varies only within certain limits. Each mineral species will therefore possess specific physical properties such as crystal form, hardness, cleavage, specific gravity, color, luster, and streak. Most physical properties are remarkably constant and develop in a mineral regardless of age or place of origin and thus constitute the fundamental criteria of mineral identification. In some minerals, however, atoms of certain related elements are interchangeable in the crystal structure in much the same way as bricks of different materials but similar size can be built into a wall without altering the structure or outward shape of the wall. Such replacement is called *solid solution,* or *isomorphism.* A mineral in which solid solution occurs will have a specific internal structure but a composition which varies within definite limits. Some physical properties are therefore variable.

One of the simplest examples of solid solution is the olivine group of minerals in which iron and magnesium can freely substitute for each other in the crystal structure. The formula is generally written $(Mg, Fe)_2SiO_4$ to express the fact that different types of olivine may have a chemical composition ranging from pure Mg_2SiO_4 to pure Fe_2SiO_4. Iron and magnesium fully substitute for each other, but the proportions of silicon and oxygen remain constant. The mineral groups in which solid solution is most important are: (1) feldspars, (2) olivines, (3) pyroxenes, (4) amphiboles, (5) garnets, and (6) micas.

Identification of Minerals

Crystal Form. In the previous exercise we saw that when a crystal is allowed to grow in an unrestricted environment, it will develop natural crystal faces which produce a perfect geometric pattern. The shape of a crystal is a reflection of the internal structure and can be used to identify many mineral species. It should be remembered, however, that two or more minerals may have essentially the same internal structure and develop similar crystals. Some of the common minerals in which crystal form is especially diagnostic are quartz, halite, garnet, fluorite, pyrite, galena, amphibole, and pyroxene.

Cleavage and Fracture. The forces which hold the atoms together in a crystalline structure are not necessarily equal in all directions. If definite planes of weakness exist, the mineral will cleave or break repeatedly along these planes much more readily than in other directions. The surface along which the break develops is referred to as the cleavage plane, and the orientation of the plane is the cleavage direction. Crystals may have one, two, three, four, or six cleavage directions equally well developed as is illustrated in Figure 4. Some minerals, such as gypsum, possess better cleavage in one direction than another.

Perfect cleavage is easily recognized, for it characteristically develops a smooth, even surface which will reflect light like a mirror (Figure 5A). Cleavage planes may occur in a steplike manner, however, and appear at first to be an irregular fracture. If the specimen is rotated in front of a light, the small, parallel cleavage planes will reflect light in the same manner as a large, smooth cleavage surface (Figure 5B). An uneven fracture will not concentrate light in any particular direction (Figure 5C).

4

A. Cleavage in one direction.
Example: muscovite.

 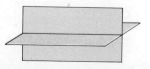

B. Cleavage in two directions at right angles.
Example: feldspar.

 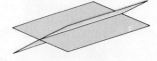

C. Cleavage in two directions not at right angles.
Example: amphibole.

 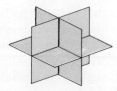

D. Cleavage in three directions at right angles.
Example: halite.

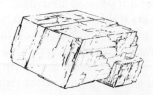

E. Cleavage in three directions not at right angles.
Example: calcite.

 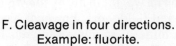

F. Cleavage in four directions.
Example: fluorite.

 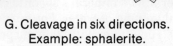

G. Cleavage in six directions.
Example: sphalerite.

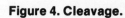

Figure 4. Cleavage.

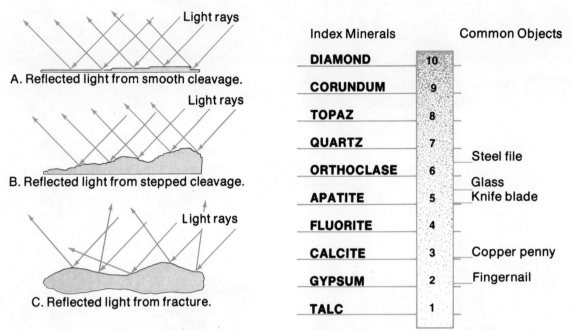

Figure 5. Reflection of light from cleavage surfaces.

Figure 6. The Mohs scale of hardness.

One must keep in mind the distinction between cleavage planes and crystal faces. Cleavage results from planes of weakness within the crystal structure along which the crystal breaks. Crystal faces reflect the geometry of the structure. Both are properties of single crystals. In a crystalline aggregate the individual crystals will break along their own cleavage planes, if any exist, but the aggregate does not possess cleavage.

In some minerals the crystalline structure is so well knit that there is no tendency to break along one plane in preference to another. Such minerals do not possess cleavage, but break or fracture in an irregular manner. Common fractures are conchoidal, irregular, and fibrous.

Hardness. Hardness, a measure of the ability of a mineral to resist abrasion, is another property related to crystal structure and interatomic bond strength. It is a relative property and one of the first used to determine unknown minerals in the field. If two minerals are rubbed together, the harder one scratches the softer. Over a century ago Friedrich Mohs, a German mineralogist, assigned an arbitrary relative number to ten common minerals. Diamond, the hardest mineral known, was placed at the top and assigned the number of 10. Softer minerals were ranked in descending order, perhaps without the realization of the unequal degree of hardness between the various ranks. If an absolute value were used, with talc as number 1, diamond would be about 42.

The Mohs scale of hardness, together with the hardness of several common articles, is shown in Figure 6 and should be referred to in determining hardness of unknown minerals. For example, calcite will scratch your fingernail, gypsum, and talc; but it will never scratch a knife blade, fluorite, or quartz.

Generally, hardness is a reliable physical property, but variations in composition may render a mineral harder or softer than normal. Moreover, because weathering may affect hardness, it is important to make tests on fresh surfaces.

Specific Gravity. Specific gravity is the ratio between the mass of a mineral and the mass of an equal volume of water. It is one of the most constant physical properties of a mineral and you can determine a mineral's specific gravity accurately by dividing its weight in air by the weight of an equal volume of water. For purposes of general laboratory and field work, however, you can estimate specific gravity with surprising accuracy by lifting a mineral specimen in your hand. Galena, with a specific gravity of approximately 7.5, and pyrite, about 5, are typical of minerals with high specific gravity, whereas common rock-forming minerals such as quartz, feldspars, and calcite have a specific gravity between 2.6 and 2.8.

Color. Color is one of the most obvious properties of a mineral, and for some, such as galena (gray), azurite (blue), and olivine (green), it is diagnostic. Other minerals are found in various hues, depending on such things as variations in composition and inclusions of impurities. Quartz, for example, ranges through a spectrum of colorless clear crystals to purple, red, white, and jet black. In brief, color may be diagnostic for a few minerals but is almost without diagnostic significance in others. Color should be considered in mineral identification but should never be used as the major identifying characteristic.

Streak. When a mineral is powdered, it usually exhibits a much more diagnostic color than when it is in large pieces. The color of the powdered mineral is referred to as streak. In the laboratory, streak is obtained by vigorously rubbing the mineral on an unglazed porcelain plate. Generally, the streak of a mineral will be different from the color seen in the hand specimen, so one should never anticipate the color of streak by visual examination of a mineral fragment.

Sometimes streak will not help in the diagnosis of a mineral. Most minerals with a nonmetallic luster have a white or pastel streak, and for this reason streak is not very useful in distinguishing nonmetallic minerals. Minerals with hardness greater than that of porcelain will scratch the plate and will not produce streak at all.

Luster. The terms "metallic" and "nonmetallic" broadly describe the basic types of luster, or the appearance of light reflected from a mineral. Pyrite and galena have a metallic luster on unweathered surfaces. A variety of nonmetallic lusters can be discriminated, the most important of which are described as vitreous, pearly, resinous, silky, and greasy. Study examples of each luster type from specimens provided by your instructor in order to become acquainted with the various luster types.

Some minerals, because of their characteristically weathered or porous nature, may not possess luster and are referred to as earthy and dull.

Tenacity. The resistance of a mineral to breakage is called tenacity. It is described by the following terms:

1. *Brittle*—crushes to angular fragments. Example: quartz.

2. *Malleable*—can be modified in shape without breaking and can be flattened to a thin sheet. Example: native copper.

3. *Sectile*—can be cut with a knife into thin shavings. Example: talc.

4. *Flexible*—will bend but does not regain its original shape when force is released. Example: selenite gypsum.

5. *Elastic*—will bend and regain its original shape when force is released. Example: muscovite and biotite.

Diaphaneity. The way in which a mineral transmits light is referred to as diaphaneity and is described as follows:

1. *Transparent*—objects are visible when viewed through a mineral. Example: some species of quartz, calcite, and biotite.

2. *Translucent*—light, but not an image, is transmitted through a mineral. Example: some varieties of gypsum.

3. *Opaque*—no light is transmitted, even on thinnest edges. Example: magnetite and pyrite.

Reaction to Hydrochloric Acid. Calcite ($CaCO_3$) is one of the most common minerals on the earth's surface and, when treated with cold dilute hydrochloric acid, it will effervesce vigorously. This simple chemical test is very diagnostic and can be used to distinguish calcite from most of the common minerals. Dolomite ($CaMg(CO_3)_2$, a mineral similar to calcite, will react with cold dilute hydrochloric acid only if the specimen is powdered.

Double Refraction. This is a property of the transparent variety of calcite whereby light passing through the crystal or cleavage fragment is broken into two rays, so that an object viewed through the mineral shows a double image.

Magnetism. Magnetite is one of the few minerals to show obvious magnetic attraction. Some other minerals have distinctive magnetic properties which can be used for mineral separation with proper equipment, but magnetite is the only common mineral that is attracted by a small magnet.

Taste. The salty taste of halite is a definite and unmistakable property of that mineral. Other evaporite minerals commonly have a bitter taste but are not exceedingly common.

Procedure

Examine each mineral specimen provided for this exercise and briefly describe its physical properties as accurately as possible. It is important to study a mineral systematically and record all properties observed even though they may be completely obvious. (1) Determine the type of luster, the color, and the streak. (2) Determine the type of crystal or the texture of crystal aggregates. (3) Test for hardness, cleavage or fracture, and other physical properties.

Do not break the specimens without permission from your instructor. After you have recorded all physical properties observed, identify the mineral by referring to the mineral identification tables (pages 9 to 11). You will note that the tables are arranged in a systematic manner. The minerals are first grouped into three categories on the basis of luster and color (Tables 1, 2, and 3). A second grouping is made on the basis of hardness or streak, and a third on the basis of cleavage or fracture. Specific minerals can then be determined from the brief description of other characteristics. For example, if you observe that a mineral is light colored, has a non-metallic luster, is softer than steel or glass but will scratch a penny, and has good cleavage in four directions, you would identify the mineral by referring to Table 3, Nonmetallic Luster, Light Color. You would next look under the list of minerals softer than glass and select the one which has four good cleavage directions. The only mineral possessing these properties is fluorite.

Colored photographs and descriptions of some of the common minerals are found on pages 12 to 18. When you have identified a mineral specimen, compare it with its picture in this manual. Note the similarities and determine which are significant physical properties. The colored photographs should serve as a study aid outside of class.

Problems

1. Explain the law of constancy of interfacial angles.

2. List the important types of physical properties of minerals.

3. Give a complete and accurate definition of a mineral.

4. What is solid solution?

5. What is the difference between a crystal face and a cleavage plane?

6. List the rock-forming minerals in which solid solution is important.

7. Give a brief definition of the term "hardness."

8. What common mineral will react with dilute HCl?

9. What is the typical crystal form of quartz?

10. Are specimens of microcrystalline quartz single crystals or aggregates of crystals?

11. What type of quartz is most common in a granite?

12. What is the most common occurrence of chert?

13. Is there a fundamental difference between milky quartz, smoky quartz, and rose quartz?

14. What are the diagnostic physical properties of the feldspars?

15. What are the two main subgroups of the feldspars? How do they differ?

16. How would you distinguish between Ca-plagioclase and K-feldspar?

17. What are the important physical properties of calcite?

18. How can microcrystalline calcite be recognized in a hand specimen?

19. What are the diagnostic properties of olivine?

20. In what rocks is olivine important?

21. How can one distinguish between amphibole and pyroxene?

22. What are the diagnostic properties of halite?

23. What are the diagnostic properties of gypsum?

24. Is a hand specimen of kaolinite an aggregate or a single crystal?

25. List the important rock-forming minerals.

TABLE 1. METALLIC LUSTER*

Gray Streak	**Perfect cubic cleavage;** heavy, Sp. Gr. = 7.6; H = 2.5; silver gray color	GALENA PbS
Black Streak	**Magnetic;** black to dark gray; Sp. Gr. = 5.2; H = 6; commonly occurs in granular masses; single crystals are octohedral	MAGNETITE Fe_3O_4
Black Streak	**Steel gray;** soft, marks paper, greasy feel; H = 1; Sp. Gr. = 2; luster may be dull	GRAPHITE C
Greenish Black Streak	**Golden yellow color;** may tarnish purple; H = 4; Sp. Gr. = 4.3	CHALCOPYRITE $CuFeS_2$
	Brass yellow; cubic crystals; common in granular aggregates; H = 6-6.5; Sp. Gr. = 5; lacks cleavage	PYRITE FeS_2
Reddish Brown Streak	**Steel gray;** black to dark brown; granular, fibrous, or micaceous aggregates; single crystals are thick plates; H = 5-6.5; Sp. Gr. = 5; lacks cleavage	HEMATITE Fe_2O_3
Yellow Brown Streak	**Yellow, brown, or black;** hard structureless or radial fibrous masses; H = 5-5.5; Sp. Gr. = 3.5-4	LIMONITE $Fe_2O_3 \cdot H_2O$

*In Tables 1, 2, and 3 the most diagnostic properties for each mineral are indicated by bold type.

TABLE 2. NONMETALLIC LUSTER—DARK COLOR

HARDER THAN GLASS	Cleavage Prominent	**Cleavage—2 directions nearly at 90°;** dark green to black; short prismatic 8-sided crystals; H = 6; Sp. Gr. = 3.5	PYROXENE GROUP Complex Ca, Mg, Fe, Al silicates **Augite** most common mineral
		Cleavage—2 directions at approx. 60° and 120°; dark green to black or brown; long prismatic 6-sided crystals; H = 6; Sp. Gr. = 3-3.5	AMPHIBOLE GROUP Complex Na, Ca, Mg, Fe, Al silicates **Hornblende** most common mineral
	Cleavage Absent	**Olive green; commonly in aggregates of small glassy grains;** conchoidal fracture; transparent to translucent; glassy luster; H = 6.5-7; Sp. Gr. = 3.5-4.5	OLIVINE $(Fe, Mg)_2SiO_4$
		Red, brown, or yellow; glassy luster; conchoidal fracture; commonly occurs in well-formed 12-sided crystals; H = 7-7.5; Sp. Gr. = 3.5-4.5	GARNET GROUP Fe, Mg, Ca, Al silicates
SOFTER THAN GLASS	Cleavage Prominent	**Brown to black; 1 perfect cleavage;** thin, flexible, elastic sheets; H = 2.5-3; Sp. Gr. = 3-3.5	BIOTITE $K(Mg,Fe)_3AlSi_3O_{10}(OH)_2$
		Green to very dark green; 1 cleavage direction; commonly occurs in foliated or scaly masses; nonelastic plates; H = 2-2.5; Sp. Gr. = 2.5-3.5	CHLORITE Hydrous Mg, Fe, Al silicate
		Yellowish brown; resinous luster; cleavage—6 directions; yellowish brown or nearly white streaks; H = 3.5-4; Sp. Gr. = 4	SPHALERITE ZnS
	Cleavage Absent	**Red; earthy appearance;** red streak; H = 1.5	HEMATITE Fe_2O_3 (earth variety)
		Yellowish brown streak; yellowish brown to dark brown; commonly in compact earth masses; H = 1.5	LIMONITE $Fe_2O_3 \cdot H_2O$

TABLE 3. NONMETALLIC LUSTER—LIGHT COLOR

HARDER THAN GLASS	Cleavage Prominent	**Good cleavage in 2 directions at approximately 90°;** pearly to vitreous luster; H = 6-6.5; Sp. Gr. = 2.5	FELDSPAR GROUP **Potassium feldspars:** $KAlSi_3O_8$—Pink, white, or green **Plagioclase feldspars:** $NaAlSi_3O_8$ to $CaAl_2Si_2O_8$—White, blue gray; striations on some cleavage planes
	Cleavage Absent	**Conchoidal fracture; H = 7;** Sp. Gr. = 2.65; transparent to translucent; vitreous luster; 6-sided prismatic crystals terminated by 6-sided triangular faces in well-developed crystals; vitreous to waxy	QUARTZ SiO_2 (silica) **Varieties:** Milky: white and opaque Smoky: gray to black Rose: light pink Amethyst: violet
		Conchoidal fracture; H = 6-6.5; variable color; translucent to opaque; dull or clouded luster	CRYPTOCRYSTALLINE QUARTZ SiO_2 **Varieties:** Agate: banded Flint: dark color Chert: light color Jasper: red Opal: waxy luster
SOFTER THAN GLASS	Cleavage Prominent	**Perfect cubic cleavage;** colorless to white; soluble in water; salty taste; H = 2-2.5; Sp. Gr. = 2	HALITE NaCl
		Perfect cleavage in 1 direction; poor in 2 others; H = 2; white; transparent; nonelastic; Sp. Gr. = 2.3; **Varieties:** Selenite: colorless, transparent; Alabaster: aggregates of small crystals; Satin spar; fibrous, silky luster	GYPSUM $CaSO_4 \cdot 2H_2O$
		Perfect cleavage in 3 directions at approximately 75°; effervesces in HCl; H = 3; colorless, white or pale yellow, rarely gray or blue; transparent to opaque; Sp. Gr. = 2.7	CALCITE $CaCO_3$ (fine-grained crystalline aggregates form limestone and marble)
		Three directions of cleavage as in calcite; effervesces in HCl only if powdered; H = 3.5-4; Sp. Gr. = 2.8; color variable but commonly white or pink rhomb-faced crystals	DOLOMITE $CaMg(CO_3)_2$
		Good cleavage in 4 directions; H = 4; Sp. Gr. = 3; colorless, yellow, blue, green, or violet; transparent to translucent; cubic crystals	FLUORITE CaF_2
		Perfect cleavage in 1 direction, producing thin, elastic sheets; H = 2-3; Sp. Gr. = 2.8; transparent and colorless in thin sheets	MUSCOVITE $KAl_2(AlSi_3O_{10}(OH)_2$
		Green to white; soapy feel; pearly luster; H = 1; Sp. Gr. = 2.8; foliated or compact masses; one direction of cleavage forms thin scales and shreds	TALC $Mg_3Si_4O_{10}(OH)_2$
	Cleavage Absent	**White to red; earthy masses;** crystals so small no cleavage visible; soft; H = 1.2; becomes plastic when moistened; earthy odor	KAOLINITE $Al_4Si_4O_{10}(OH)_8$

Quartz

Quartz is one of the most common minerals in the earth's crust, as it is a major constituent in many igneous, sedimentary, and metamorphic rocks. If allowed to grow in an unrestricted environment, it will form well-develped hexagonal (six-sided) crystals which terminate in a pyramid. In most igneous rocks and in veins, quartz is one of the last minerals to form, so it fills interstices between other minerals and thus has an irregular shape. The color, crystal size, and general appearance of quartz will vary greatly, so that a large number of varieties have been named. These can be classified into two major groups: (1) macrocrystalline quartz and (2) crypto-crystalline quartz. Further subdivision in each group can be made on the basis of color or some other special feature. Regardless of color, crystal size, shape, mode of origin, etc., *all quartz is characterized by: (1) a hardness of 7 (it will scratch glass and steel), (2) conchoidal fracture, and (3) glassy luster.*

Macrocrystalline Quartz. Macrocrystalline quartz is composed of individual crystals which can be seen with the naked eye, or with low-power magnification. Varieties are distinguished mainly on the basis of color.

Figure 7. Cluster of quartz crystals—Quartz commonly develops in groups of slender, six-sided prisms which terminate in a pyramid. Striations are common across the prism faces. Crystals are usually milky, colorless, or transparent.

Figure 8. Quartz crystals—Quartz crystals will grow to a wide variety of sizes, shapes, and colors. In every quartz crystal, regardless of where, when, or how it grew, the angles between corresponding crystal faces are identical.

Figure 9. Amethyst—Transparent quartz crystals in hues of purple and violet are commonly referred to as amethyst. It usually develops as a secondary mineral in veins and cavities. The color is due to small inclusions of ferric iron.

Figure 10. Milky quartz—Milky quartz is commonly massive and occurs in veins without well-developed crystal faces. Minute fluid inclusions are responsible for its white color.

Figure 11. Smoky quartz—Smoky quartz is a brown, gray, or black quartz characteristic of intrusive igneous rocks. It is transparent to translucent. Radiation from radioactive minerals will develop a smoky appearance in colorless quartz and may be responsible for much smoky quartz in nature.

Figure 12. Rose quartz—Small amounts of titanium appear to be the coloring agent in rose quartz. This variety of quartz is generally coarsely crystalline, transparent to translucent, but rarely forms well-developed crystals.

Figure 13. Quartz in granite—Quartz is one of the last minerals to form in granite and thus fills spaces between crystals formed earlier. It is characterized by glassy luster and conchoidal fracture and is usually smoky.

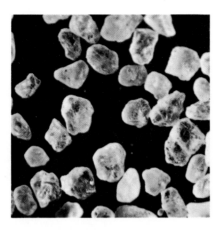

Figure 14. Quartz in sandstone—Most sand grains are crystals of quartz which have been abraded by wind and water. Some grains may be frosted, but broken grains show glassy luster and conchoidal fracture.

Figure 15. Quartz in quartzite—Heat and pressure may fuse sand grains together to form a dense massive rock called quartzite. This rock is very resistant to weathering and abrasion, so quartzite pebbles are common constituents of gravel.

Cryptocrystalline Quartz (Chalcedony). All cryptocrystalline quartz is composed of aggregates of innumerable submicroscopic crystals. Color variations give rise to many varieties.

Figure 16. Chert—Chert is a light-colored variety of chalcedony which usually occurs as nodules in limestone.

Figure 17. Flint—Flint is similar to chert but is characterized by its dark color. Both break with a conchoidal fracture.

Figure 18. Agate—Agate is a variety of chalcedony in which colorful banding is due to successive periods of deposition.

Figure 19. Jasper—Minute inclusions of hematite impart a red color which distinguishes jasper from other varieties of cryptocrystalline quartz.

Figure 20. Opal—Opal contains variable amounts of water and is distinguished from other varieties of cryptocrystalline quartz by its waxy luster.

Figure 21. Petrified wood—Cryptocrystalline quartz commonly replaces organic material in the process of fossilization. In petrified wood many delicate structures are preserved because of the small crystal size.

The Feldspar Group

The feldspars are the most abundant mineral in the earth's crust, and, like quartz, they are a basic constituent for many igneous, sedimentary, and metamorphic rocks. All are aluminum silicates of either potassium, sodium, or calcium and are closely related in form and physical properties. Two main subgroups are recognized: the *plagioclase feldspars*, which range in composition from $CaAl_2Si_2O_8$ to $NaAlSi_3O_8$ as a solid solution series, and the *potassium feldspars*, with a composition of $KAlSi_3O_8$, but variations occur in the arrangement of Al and Si ions in the crystal structure. Distinction between varieties of feldspars can be made best by a chemical analysis, or optical or x-ray measurements of the crystal structure. The color is due to small amounts of iron or magnesium and certain aspects of the crystal structure and is not diagnostic of a particular variety. *The most important physical properties of the feldspars are:(1) two-directional cleavage at approximately right angles, (2) hardness of 6, and (3) pearly luster.*

Figure 22. Sodium plagioclase (albite)—Sodium plagioclase feldspar is commonly light colored and has a porcelain luster. The two-directional cleavage, characteristic of all feldspars, is generally well expressed.

Figure 23. Calcium plagioclase (labradorite)—Striations on certain cleavage surfaces are diagnostic of calcium plagioclase and serve to distinguish this group from the potassium feldspars. Calcium plagioclase is dark colored and shows iridescence.

Figure 24. Potassium feldspar—Although color is not diagnostic, most pink and green feldspars belong to the potassium subgroup. Well-developed cleavage in two directions is similar to that in plagioclase feldspar.

Figure 25. Feldspar in granite—Potassium feldspar is a major constituent of granite and is commonly expressed by rectangular pink crystals. Sodium feldspar in granite is characteristically white. Both may occur in the same specimen.

Figure 26. Feldspars in sandstone—Weathering and erosion of a granite will disaggregate the feldspar and quartz. Feldspars rapidly break down to form clay minerals and therefore are not common constituents of sediments. Angular grains of feldspar, however, are found in some sandstones deposited adjacent to a granite source area.

Figure 27. Photomicrograph of feldspar in basalt (length of field = 8 mm)—Many fine-grained, dark-colored igneous rocks (basalts) contain large amounts of plagioclase in crystals too small to be seen in hand specimens. Under the microscope, however, the plagioclase feldspars appear as elongate rectangular crystals in a felt-like fabric.

Calcite and Dolomite

Calcite is a major rock-forming mineral and may appear in a great variety of forms. It occurs as thick, widespread masses of limestone, chalk, and marble and is commonly deposited in caves, in hot and cold springs, and in veins. Physical properties which serve to distinguish it from other minerals, regardless of the form in which it is expressed, are: *(1) hardness of 3 on the Mohs scale, (2) perfect rhombohedral cleavage, and (3) reaction with dilute hydrochloric acid.* Calcite is thus one of the easiest minerals to identify. The major problem for the beginning student is to become familiar with the wide variety of forms in which it may occur.

Figure 28. Calcite crystals—Crystals of calcite are extremely variable in form. They may be tabular, hexagonal, pyramidal, or rhombohedral. Large crystals develop in veins and other voids, whereas the form of calcite in most limestones usually consists of compact aggregates of very small crystals.

Figure 29. Rhombohedron of clear calcite—The perfect rhombohedral cleavage of calcite is one of its most distinctive properties. Regardless of crystal form or mode of occurrence, all calcite will cleave perfectly in three directions not at right angles. Most calcite is white, although various impurities may tint it almost any color or even black. Colorless, clear calcite shows strong double refraction.

Figure 30. Crystalline limestone—Calcite is the dominant mineral in limestones; in some formations, it is the only mineral present. It may occur as interlocking crystals which range in size from submicroscopic to over an inch long. A variety of additional forms of calcite in limestones is discussed and illustrated on pages 44-45.

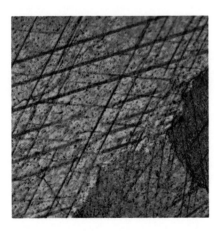

Figure 31. Photomicrograph of calcite (length of field = 8 mm)—The physical properties of a mineral are commonly well expressed on a microscopic scale. In this specimen of limestone, perfect rhombohedral cleavage is clearly seen in the three interlocking grains.

Figure 32. Fracture filled with calcite—Calcite is one of the most soluble of the common minerals. Both surface and ground water are able to dissolve large quantities of this mineral in a relatively short period of time. Calcite may be subsequently precipitated from solution and fill cavities and fractures such as the light calcite veins shown above.

Figure 33. Dolomite crystals—Dolomite $CaMg(CO_3)_2$ is a carbonate mineral similar in many respects to calcite. Crystals are usually rhombohedral and occur as large cleavable forms of fine, compact aggregates. Pure dolomite is usually pink, but it may be colorless, white, gray, green, or black. Dolomite is distinguished from calcite in that it will effervesce in HCl only in a powdered form.

Other Rock-Forming Minerals

Figure 34. Aggregate of olivine crystals —Olivine ranges in composition from Mg_2SiO_4 to Fe_2SiO_4, there being a complete solid solution of Mg and Fe in the the crystal structure. The most common varieties of olivine are rich in Mg. They are characterized by olive green color and equidimensional glassy grains which lack cleavage. Olivine commonly occurs in aggregates. It is not exceedingly abundant, but it is an important mineral in dark-colored igneous rocks such as basalt.

Figure 35. Pyroxene crystals—Pyroxenes are complex silicates containing substantial amounts of Ca, Mg, and Fe. They are green to black or brown in color. Crystals are short and stubby and when seen in cross section appear nearly square. Two cleavage planes intersect at right angles. Both cleavage and crystal form are generally poorly expressed in hand specimen, but are well defined microscopically. Pyroxenes are essential constituents of dark-colored igneous rocks rich in iron and are common in very high-grade metamorphic rocks.

Figure 36. Cleavage fragment of amphibole—Amphiboles are complex silicates having a composition similar to that of pyroxene but containing water. Many physical properties of the two mineral groups are therefore similar. Amphiboles may be distinguished by long, columnar crystals and visible cleavage in two directions intersecting at 56° and 124°. Amphibole (in particular the variety hornblende) is common as phenocrysts in gray lavas (andesites).

Figure 37. Muscovite—The micas are a distinctive group of minerals with cleavage so perfect in one direction that each crystal can be separated into sheets thinner than a piece of paper. The two leading varieties are: (1) *muscovite,* or white mica, and (2) *biotite,* or dark mica.

Figure 38. Biotite—In addition to its perfect cleavage, mica is characterized by a pearly to vitreous luster. The cleavage sheets are elastic and flexible, and the mineral is notably soft. Micas are common in light-colored granitic rocks, and to a lesser extent in light-colored volcanics. They are also widespread in a variety of low- to intermediate-grade metamorphic rocks and impure sandstones.

Figure 39. Aggregate of chlorite crystals —Chlorite is a common metamorphic mineral resulting from alteration of silicates, such as pyroxene, amphibole, biotite, or garnet. It is characteristically dark green in color and occurs in aggregates of minute crystals or finely disseminated particles. Individual crystals have perfect cleavage in one direction which produces small, scaly, nonelastic plates.

Figure 40. Garnet—The garnet group includes a series of silicate minerals which characteristically occur in well-formed, subspherical, twelve-sided crystals. They are hard (7-7.5 on the Mohs scale) and are commonly red, although brown, yellow, green, and black varieties occur, depending on composition. Garnets have no cleavage, but may fracture along subparallel surfaces. The dominant fracture, however, is conchoidal. Most garnets are translucent to transparent and have a vitreous luster. They are typical minerals of metamorphic rocks.

Figure 41. Talc—Talc is a secondary mineral formed from the alteration of magnesium silicates such as olivine, pyroxene, and amphiboles. It is distinguished from other minerals by its extreme softness (1 on the Mohs scale), greasy feel, and perfect cleavage in one direction. Talc usually occurs as white to green foliated masses. The cleavage flakes are nonelastic.

Figure 42. Serpentine—Serpentine is commonly compact and massive, and often multicolored. A fibrous variety (asbestos) consists of delicate, fine, parallel fibers which can easily be separated. It is usually found in veins.

Figure 43. Halite—Halite is common salt (NaCl). It is characterized by cubic crystals which are usually clear and transparent, but impurities may impart reddish hues. It has perfect cleavage in three directions at right angles, and a hardness between 2 and 2.5. Halite is by far the most common water-soluble mineral. It is precipitated from sea water or saline lakes by evaporation and accumulates as salt beds interstratified with gypsum, silt, or shale. Salt layers may flow under pressure and squeeze up in weak places, forming pluglike bodies of solid salt (salt domes of the Gulf coast and elsewhere).

Figure 44. Selenite gypsum—Gypsum is a common sedimentary mineral formed by evaporation of sea water or saline lakes. It is generally colorless to white and has a glassy to silky luster. Crystals are tabular. Gypsum is further characterized by its softness (2 on the Mohs scale) and three unequal cleavage planes, one of which is perfect. Cleavage sheets are nonelastic. Varieties of gypsum include *satin spar,* fibrous gypsum with silky luster; *alabaster,* aggregates of fine crystals; and *selenite,* large, colorless, transparent crystals.

Figure 45. Kaolinite—Kaolinite is one of several clay minerals which form from the decomposition of aluminum silicates—especially feldspar. It occurs in earthy aggregates of nearly submicroscopic, platy crystals. In hand specimens it appears claylike and is usually chalk white, although it may be stained red, brown, or black. It has a dull, earthy luster and disaggregates easily. Masses of kaolinite can be cut or shaped with a knife.

Metallic Minerals

Figure 46. Pyrite—Pyrite is a yellow metallic mineral composed of FeS_2 which commonly crystallizes into cubes. It has a hardness between 6 and 6.5 and breaks with a conchoidal fracture.

Figure 47. Chalcopyrite—Chalcopyrite is a metallic mineral composed of copper, iron, and sulfur. It is characterized by a brass yellow color, which is often tarnished and appears slightly iridescent.

Figure 48. Galena—Galena (lead sulfide) is the most important lead mineral. It commonly crystallizes into cubes and is easily recognized by perfect cubic cleavage and high specific gravity (7.5).

Figure 49. Graphite—Graphite is composed of carbon atoms united in a sheet-like structure. It commonly occurs as foliated masses and is distinguished by extreme softness, perfect cleavage in one direction, and greasy feel.

Figure 50. Sphalerite—Sphalerite is the most important zinc mineral. It is difficult to recognize because of its extremely variable color (yellow, red, brown to black). The most diagnostic properties are its resinous luster and perfect cleavage in six directions.

Figure 51. Native copper—Native copper usually crystallizes in malformed cubes, producing an irregular mass, twisted and wirelike in form. It has a copper color and metallic luster and is highly ductile and malleable.

Figure 52. Magnetite—Magnetite is a common ore of iron and the only mineral that is strongly magnetic. Other diagnostic properties are its black color, hardness (6 on the Mohs scale), and black streak.

Figure 53. Hematite—Hematite is an iron mineral of widely varied appearance. Three varieties are especially common: (1) specular hematite (metallic luster), (2) earthy hematite, and (3) oolitic hematite. All are characterized by a deep red streak.

Figure 54. Limonite—Limonite is a yellowish brown, hydrous iron oxide resulting from alteration or weathering of previously existing iron minerals. It is amorphous and commonly occurs in both earthy and metallic varieties. The most diagnostic feature of limonite is its yellowish brown streak.

3 Igneous Rocks

In this exercise emphasis is placed on recognition and interpretation of igneous rocks. Because these rocks solidify from hot molten material (magma), direct observation of igneous rock formation is limited to extrusive igneous materials such as those associated with volcanic activity. Significant knowledge of the environments and conditions under which magmas form and eventually solidify has been achieved, however, based upon studies of *composition* and *texture* of igneous rocks. Considerable attention will be focused on these two properties in this exercise. Once one develops the ability to correctly use them, recognition and interpretation of igneous rocks can be achieved.

Composition

Approximately 99 percent of the total bulk of most igneous rocks is made up of only eight elements—oxygen, silicon, aluminum, iron, calcium, sodium, potassium, and magnesium. Most of these elements enter into the crystal structure of rock-forming silicate minerals and form feldspars, olivines, pyroxenes, amphiboles, quartz, and mica. *These six minerals constitute over 95 percent of the volume of all common igneous rocks and are therefore of paramount importance in a study of their classification and origin.* Magmas rich in iron, magnesium, and calcium are referred to as *mafic* (magnesium and iron) and produce greater quantities of olivine, pyroxene, amphibole, and calcium plagioclase. These rocks are dark colored because of the abundant dark ferromagnesian minerals. Magmas rich in silica and aluminum are referred to as *sialic* and tend to produce more quartz, potassium feldspar, and sodium plagioclase, which generally form light-colored rocks. It is possible, therefore, to approximate *(and only approximate, for there are many exceptions)*, the mineral composition of igneous rocks by color.

Three major mineralogical criteria are used for recognition of igneous rocks.

1. The presence or absence of quartz—*Quartz is an essential mineral in sialic rocks, whereas it is an accessory mineral in intermediate and mafic rocks.*

2. The composition of the feldspars—*Potassium feldspars and sodium plagioclase are essential minerals in sialic rocks but are rare or absent in intermediate and mafic rocks. Calcium plagioclase is characteristic of mafic rocks.*

3. The proportion and kinds of ferromagnesian minerals—*As a general rule, mafic rocks are rich in ferromagnesian minerals while sialic rocks are rich in quartz. Olivine is generally restricted to mafic rocks; pyroxenes and amphiboles range through mafic to intermediate rocks. Biotite is common in intermediate and sialic rocks.*

Crystallization of minerals from a magma occurs between 1200° and 600° C. Minerals with the highest freezing point crystallize first and have a greater freedom to develop well-formed crystal faces. Minerals crystallizing at a lower temperature are forced to grow within the space between early-formed crystals and are characteristically irregular in shape with few well-developed crystal faces. From laboratory studies with artificial magmas and from petrographic studies of igneous rocks a general order of crystallization has been recognized. This sequence is summarized in Figure 55 and is fundamental to the study of igneous rocks.

It is apparent from the order of crystallization that in a mafic magma, olivine and calcium plagioclase are the first materials to form, followed by pyroxenes, amphiboles, and sodium

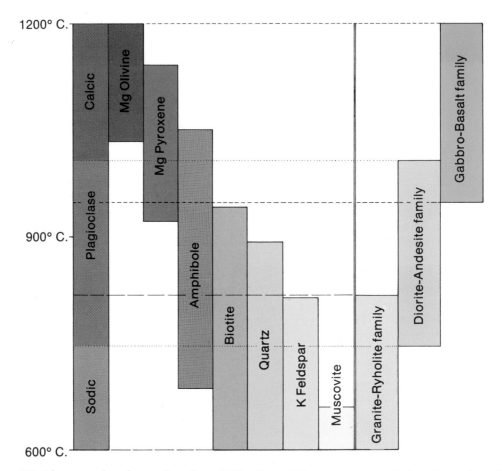

Figure 55. Diagram showing order of crystallization of the common rock-forming minerals.

plagioclase. Such a magma will produce rocks of the gabbro-basalt family and will crystallize between 900° and 1200° C. In magmas rich in silica and aluminum, biotite and potassium feldspar form first, followed by quartz and muscovite. Rocks of the granite-rhyolite family develop from such a magma at temperatures below 900° C.

Textures

Texture refers to the size, shape, and boundary relations between adjacent minerals in a rock mass. In most igneous rocks the texture has an overall aspect of a network of interlocking crystals. This is especially obvious in rocks containing large crystals but is also expressed nicely in thin sections of fine-grained rocks when viewed under the microscope (see Figures 68 and 69).

Textures of igneous rocks develop primarily in response to composition and rate of cooling of the magma. Magmas located deep within the earth's crust cool very slowly. Individual crystals are more or less uniform in size and may grow to an inch or more in diameter. A magma extruded out upon the earth's surface, in contrast, cools rapidly and the crystals have only a short time to grow. Crystals from such a magma are typically so small that they can rarely be seen without the aid of a microscope, and the rock appears massive and structureless. If extremely rapid cooling took place, as would result if a lava flowed into the sea or a lake, the magma would be quenched and crystals would have little or no time to form. The rock resulting from such a process would be a supercooled solution or a natural glass. An additional textural type may develop if the cooling history is more complex, involving a period of slow cooling followed by a period of more rapid cooling. Two distinct crystal sizes would probably develop; the large crystals, called *phenocrysts*, develop during the period of slower cooling and are surrounded by smaller crystals, which form during the period of rapid cooling.

The size of crystals is also influenced to a considerable degree by the viscosity of the magma. Experimental studies, together with direct field observation, show that magmas rich in silica are characteristically viscous and develop small crystals, whereas magmas deficient in silica are more fluid, so larger crystals may develop. Viscosity is also influenced by the amount of volatile material such as water vapor contained in the magma. As a general rule, a magma containing a high percent of volatiles will be more fluid and permit larger crystals to grow.

Textures of igneous rocks are subdivided into the following types: (1) phaneritic, (2) porphyritic-phaneritic, (3) aphanitic, (4) porphyritic-aphanitic, (5) glassy, and (6) fragmental.

Phaneritic Textures. Phaneritic textures are those in which individual crystals are large enough to be plainly visible to the naked eye (Figure 56).

Porphyritic-Phaneritic Textures. A porphyritic-phaneritic texture is characterized by two distinct sizes of crystals, both of which can be seen with the naked eye. The smaller crystals constitute a *matrix* or *groundmass* and surround the larger crystals, termed *phenocrysts* (Figure 57).

Aphanitic Textures. In aphanitic textures individual crystals are so small they cannot be detected without the aid of a microscope. Rocks of this texture appear massive and structureless (Figure 58) but contain small interlocking crystals (Figure 68).

Porphyritic-Aphanitic Textures. A porphyritic-aphanitic texture is one in which phenocrysts are set in an aphanitic matrix (Figure 59).

Glassy Textures. This texture is similar to that of ordinary glass. It may occur in massive units (Figure 60A) or in a threadlike mesh similar to spun glass. A glassy texture does not contain crystals even when viewed under high magnification.

Fragmental Textures. Fragmental textures consist of broken, angular fragments of ejected igneous material, ranging from large blocks to fine dust. The rock may contain fragments of the wall rock surrounding the vent, but it is composed mostly of fragments of ash, pumice, and aphanitic rocks. Material finer than 4 mm is called tuff, whereas that larger than 4 mm is referred to as volcanic breccia (Figure 61).

Phaneritic Textures

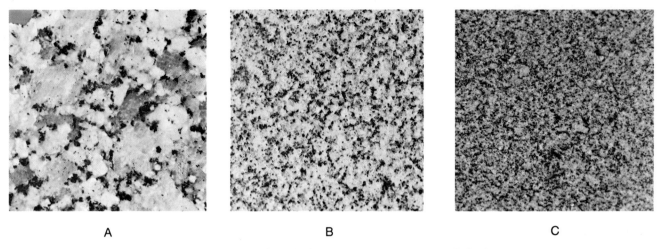

A   B   C

Figure 56. Examples of phaneritic textures (actual size).

The specimens shown above are typical of phaneritic textures. All are composed of crystals large enough to be seen with the naked eye. In Specimen A, the major constituents, quartz and feldspar, are approximately equal in size, ranging from one-fourth to one-half inch long. They interlock so that well-developed crystal faces are not present. Crystals of the minor mineral, biotite, are somewhat smaller, but the rock as a whole is equigranular and coarse grained. In Specimens B and C the individual crystals are much smaller but can still be detected. The textures are therefore properly considered phaneritic.

Phaneritic textures develop from magmas which cool slowly and commonly develop in intrusive igneous bodies such as batholiths and stocks. Very coarse phaneritic rocks in which crystals are several feet long are almost invariably found in large patches or veins.

A   B   C

Figure 57. Examples of porphyritic-phaneritic textures (actual size).

A porphyritic-phaneritic texture is one in which large phenocrysts occur in a phaneritic matrix. In Specimen A, large rectangular phenocrysts of pink potassium feldspar over three-fourths of an inch long are surrounded by a matrix of white feldspar, quartz, and ferromagnesian minerals less than one-fourth inch long. All crystals are large enough to be seen. In Specimen B, phenocrysts of pink feldspar are approximately one-half inch long and are surrounded by a matrix in which crystals are much smaller. Specimen C contains phenocrysts of euhedral crystals of amphibole (hornblende) set in a matrix of fine-grained plagioclase and ferromagnesian minerals. All specimens have a porphyritic-phaneritic texture, although the sizes of the matrix and phenocrysts differ.

Aphanitic Textures

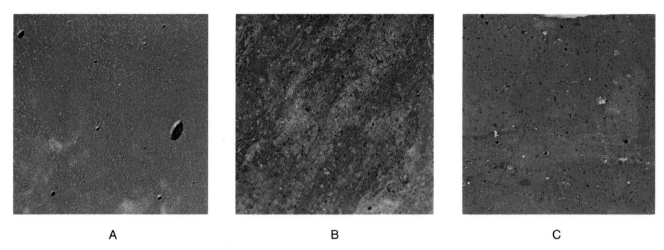

| A | B | C |

Figure 58. Examples of aphanitic textures (actual size).

In aphanitic textures individual crystals are so small they cannot be detected without the aid of a microscope. The rock therefore appears to be dense and structureless. When a thin section of an aphanitic rock is viewed under the microscope, it is readily apparent that the rock is crystalline, being composed of numerous small crystals and usually some glass. Examples of aphanitic texture seen under the microscope are shown in the photomicrographs in Figures 62 and 68.

In Specimen A above, there is some suggestion of crystallinity but one could not identify a given crystal. Flow structures are common in some aphanitic textures such as shown in Specimen B. A few phenocrysts are also common (Specimen C). Vesicles (spherical holes formed by gas bubbles as the rock cools) form near the tops of many lava flows and impart a cellular aspect to the rock (see hand specimen, Figure 68).

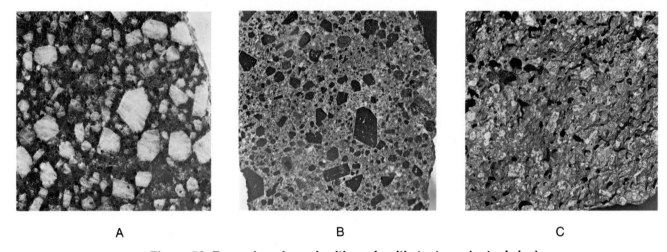

| A | B | C |

Figure 59. Examples of porphyritic-aphanitic textures (actual size).

A porphyritic-aphanitic texture consists of an aphanitic matrix with more than 10 percent phenocrysts. The phenocrysts are visible to the unaided eye and, if abundant, they may cause the rock to appear at first glance to be phaneritic. An example of this is shown in Specimen A, which consists of many large phenocrysts of white feldspar set in a dark gray matrix. Careful study of the area between the phenocrysts indicates an aphanitic matrix. In Specimen B, large, well-formed crystals of amphibole are surrounded by an aphanitic matrix. The rock in Specimen C contains many vesicles (black holes), but the aphanitic matrix contains numerous phenocrysts of green olivine. (See Figure 69, microscopic view of porphyritic-aphanitic texture.)

Glassy Textures

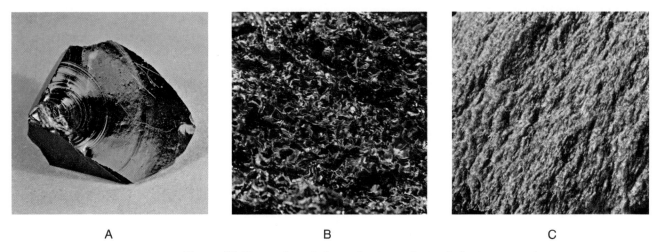

A   B   C

Figure 60. Examples of glassy textures (actual size).

Most characteristics of glassy texture in igneous rocks, such as a bright vitreous luster and conchoidal fracture with razor-sharp edges, are similar to those of ordinary glass. Technically, a glassy texture is noncrystalline. Natural glass may occur as a dense mass such as Specimen A, which is transparent along thin edges. Glassy textures in which the glass occurs as tangled, threadlike filaments may also be cellular. In such rocks there is a large amount of pore space formed by escaping gases as the lava cools. This type of glassy texture is shown in Specimens B and C.

Fragmental Textures

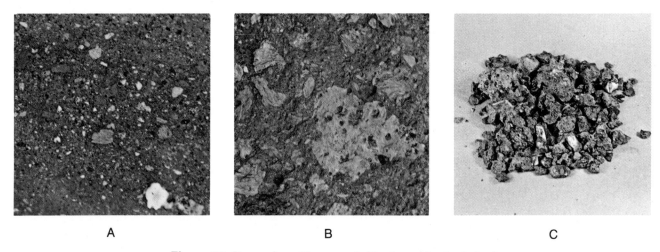

A   B   C

Figure 61. Examples of fragmental textures (actual size).

Fragmental textures are similar to clastic textures of sedimentary rock in that they consist of broken pieces of rock material. In pyroclastic rocks the fragmental material is characteristically angular and is composed of much pumice, glass, and broken crystals. Some sorting and stratification are generally present. In Specimen A, the green and white angular fragments are pumice; the pink material is fragments of aphanitic rock. A similar fragmental texture is shown in Specimen B, in which most large fragments are pumice. Recent, unconsolidated volcanic ash which develops fragmental texture when consolidated is shown in Specimen C. This material is characteristically vesicular and glassy.

Classification and Identification of Igneous Rocks

The most useful and significant system of classifying igneous rocks is based on two criteria—composition and texture. The importance of these criteria lies not only in their usefulness in describing the rock so that it can be distinguished and set apart from other rock types, named, and analyzed, but also in their important genetic implications. Mineral composition provides important clues concerning the nature of the magma, and textures are indicative of cooling history.

A chart (Table 4) in which variations in composition are shown horizontally and textural variations vertically provides an effective system of classifying and naming igneous rocks. To use this chart effectively one should proceed as follows:

1. Examine the rock and determine the type of texture. This will enable you to refer to the rock as (a) pyroclastic, (b) glassy, (c) aphanitic, (d) porphyritic-aphanitic, (e) phaneritic, or (f) porphyritic-phaneritic.

2. Determine the percent of dark minerals. This will enable you to refer to the rock as (a) silicic—few dark minerals, general light or gray color: (b) intermediate—nearly 50 percent dark minerals, dark gray color; or (c) mafic—over 70 percent dark minerals, very dark to black.

3. Determine the approximate percent and type of feldspar. (a) Pink feldspar is almost invariably a potasssium feldspar. (b) White or gray feldspar may be either potasssium feldspar or plagioclase. If the feldspar has striations, it is definitely plagioclase.

4. Determine the approximate percent of quartz. (a) 10 to 40 percent quartz—granite-rhyolite family; (b) less than 10 percent quartz—diorite-andesite family; (c) no quartz—gabbro-basalt family.

5. Use the rock chart and determine the rock name.

   Example: (a) A phaneritic rock composed of 25 percent olivine, 50 percent pyroxene, and 25 percent plagioclase would be a gabbro. (See graph of mineral composition at top of Table 4.)

   (b) An aphanitic rock containing phenocrysts of amphibole in a light-colored matrix, presumably plagioclase, would probably be a porphyritic andesite; one containing phenocrysts of quartz would be a porphyritic rhyolite.

   (c) A phaneritic rock containing 15 percent amphibole, no quartz, and 85 percent plagioclase would be a diorite.

TABLE 4.   CLASSIFICATION OF IGNEOUS ROCKS

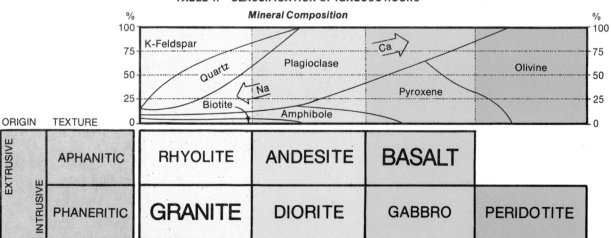

Aphanitic rocks have few distinguishable crystals and are difficult to identify with certainty in hand specimens alone. The following guidelines may be useful:

1. If quartz phenocrysts are present, the rock is a rhyolite.

2. If potassium feldspar phenocrysts are present, the rock is a rhyolite.

3. If amphibole phenocrysts are present, the rock is an andesite.

4. If pyroxene or olivine phenocrysts are present, the rock is a basalt.

If phenocrysts are conspicuous, the texture is porphyritic and the adjective "porphyritic" is added to the rock name (i.e., porphyritic granite, porphyritic basalt, etc.).

Some types of igneous rocks do not fit in well with the system used in Table 4. The most important of these rocks are described below:

OBSIDIAN— A massive volcanic glass usually jet black due to dustlike particles of magnetite and ferromagnesian minerals. Most obsidian is rich in silica and has a *chemical* composition similar to that of granite and rhyolite.

PUMICE— A porous volcanic glass with a texture consisting of subparallel glass fibers tangled together.

TUFF and BRECCIA—Fragmental volcanic rocks form from consolidation of volcanic ash. Tuff is fine grained, as sand or a shale is. Breccia is coarse grained, as a conglomerate is. Composition is variable.

Granite-Rhyolite Family

The granite-rhyolite family is characterized by the following mineral composition:

Quartz 10-40%
Potassium Feldspar 30-60%
Plagioclase 0-33%
Biotite and Amphibole 10-33%

Magmas, from which these rocks are derived, are high in potassium, silicon, and sodium and are low in iron, magnesium, and calcium. Granites and rhyolites are therefore characteristically light colored.

RHYOLITE. Rhyolite is the microcrystalline extrusive equivalent of a granite formed at or near the surface. It is characteristically white, gray, or pink and nearly always contains a few phenocrysts of feldspar or quartz (2 to 10%) (Figure 62). If phenocrysts constitute more than 10 percent of the volume, the rock is properly termed **porphyritic rhyolite.** Because the texture is aphanitic, the only minerals that can be identified in a rhyolite hand specimen are those occurring as phenocrysts.

Figure 62 is from a typical rhyolite deposit of the western United States. A few small, dark phenocrysts can be seen, but most of the rock has a characteristic aphanitic texture. In thin section, flow structures are readily apparent and a considerable amount of glass is seen in the fine-grained crystals.

Magmas from which rhyolites crystallize are characteristically viscous and move very slowly compared to basaltic lavas.

GRANITE. Granite (Figure 63) is probably the most familiar of all igneous rocks. Its texture is phaneritic but the average crystal size ranges from less than one-half inch to more than one inch in diameter. Biotite, amphibole, and plagioclase (early-formed crystals) are generally euhedral (i.e., have well-developed crystal faces), whereas quartz and potassium feldspars are anhedral (i.e., have poorly developed crystal faces). In Figure 63 the white crystals are sodium feldspar, the light crystals are quartz, and the dark crystals are biotite. The equigranular texture of granite is well expressed in Figure 63. Note the interlocking nature of the euhedral crystals.

Phenocrysts in granites are usually pink potassium feldspar (Figure 64). If they occur in significant amounts, the rock is properly termed **porphyritic granite.** Most granites are gray, but if potassium feldspar dominates in the rock it may be pink or red. Figure 64 shows large euhedral phenocrysts of pink feldspar in a fine-grained matrix.

Hand specimen

Photomicrograph (X20)

Figure 62. Rhyolite.

Quartz and feldspar expressing flow lines

Hand specimen

Photomicrograph (X20)

Figure 63. Granite.

Quartz   K feldspar

Hand specimen

Photomicrograph (X20)

Figure 64. Porphyritic granite.

Feldspar   Quartz

Figure 65. Porphyritic andesite.

Photomicrograph (X20)

Feldspar

Hand specimen

Figure 66. Diorite.

Photomicrograph (X20)

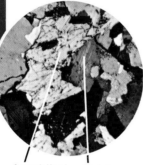

Amphibole   Feldspar

Hand specimen

Figure 67. Porphyritic diorite.

Photomicrograph (X20)

Feldspar   Ferromagnesian
minerals

Diorite-Andesite Family

The diorite-andesite family is intermediate in composition between the families of granite-rhyolite and gabbro-basalt. It is characterized by the following composition:

Plagioclase 55-70%
Amphibole and Biotite 25-40%

Plagioclase is approximately 50 percent albite and 50 percent anorthite. Potassium feldspar and quartz are present only in minor amounts. The diorite-andesite family is therefore characteristically gray in color.

ANDESITES. Andesites are generally dark gray, green, or red. Upon weathering they may become dark brown or reddish brown. Completely aphanitic andesite is relatively rare, since most flows contain some phenocrysts. Porphyritic andesite is the most common variety of intermediate extrusive rocks. Phenocrysts are composed mainly of plagioclase, amphibole, or biotite set in a matrix of aphanitic plagioclase and some glass.

Large phenocrysts of plagioclase (white) and smaller phenocrysts of amphibole (black) are shown in Figure 65. In thin section, rectangular phenocrysts of feldspar are surrounded by a fine crystalline matrix with considerable amounts of glass (dark areas). Porphyritic andesite together with basalt comprises 95 percent of all volcanic material. Andesites are abundant in the Andes Mountains of South America and most other continental margins adjacent to subduction zones.

DIORITE. The texture of diorite is essentially the same as that of granite. (Compare Figures 63 and 66.) The two rocks differ only in composition. Whereas granite contains potassium feldspar, quartz, and calcium plagioclase, diorite is composed predominantly of plagioclase and ferromagnesian minerals. In Figure 66, ferromagnesian minerals make up a greater proportion of the rock and give it a darker color. In thin section (Figure 66), quartz and potassium feldspar are absent, whereas plagioclase (gray mineral) and amphibole (yellowish gray mineral) predominate. Quartz occurs in amounts less than 5 percent of the total volume.

Diorite occurs in large intrusives such as complete batholiths or in peripheral parts of smaller granite bodies. It is also found in dikes, sills, and laccoliths.

Figure 67 illustrates a porphyritic diorite in which the phenocrysts are euhedral crystals of amphibole. Plagioclase may also occur as phenocrysts.

Hand specimen

Figure 68. Basalt.

Photomicrograph (X20)

Feldspar

Hand specimen

Figure 69. Porphyritic basalt.

Photomicrograph (X20)

Olivine   Feldspar

Hand specimen

Figure 70. Gabbro.

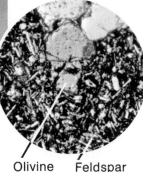

Photomicrograph (X20)

Feldspar Pyroxene

Gabbro-Basalt Family

The composition of the gabbro-basalt family is as follows:

Plagioclase (mostly Ca) 45-70%
Ferromagnesian Minerals
(olivine, pyroxene, and
amphibole)........................25-50%

These rocks crystallize from magmas relatively high in iron, magnesium, and calcium but deficient in silica. They are characteristically black or dark green in color.

BASALT. Basalt is one of the easiest rocks to recognize, because it is characteristically black, dense, and massive. Individual crystals cannot be seen with the naked eye, but under the microscope (Figure 68) tiny needles of plagioclase crystals commonly form a feltlike network surrounding crystals of pyroxene and olivine. Many basalts are clinkerlike in appearance, with about half of the total volume consisting of small holes termed *vesicles* (Figure 68). Vesicular textures develop as gases rise toward the top of the flow and are trapped in the cooling lava. Highly vesicular basalts are sometimes referred to as *scoria*. In some of the older flows, vesicles are filled with mineral deposits.

Most basalts have some phenocrysts. In Figure 69 the phenocrysts are pyroxene, but olivine phenocrysts are also common. In the thin section (Figure 69), large olivine phenocrysts are surrounded by needles of plagioclase. Plagioclase may also occur as phenocrysts, and, in some rocks, crystals may be over two inches long.

Basalt is the most abundant extrusive rock. It constitutes the bedrock for all of the oceanic crust and is also found in great floods upon some of the continents. Basaltic magma forms from partial melting of the upper mantle and is extruded most extensively along rifts.

GABBRO. Gabbros are normally composed of coarse- to medium-grained subhedral crystals. Labradorite plagioclase is the dominant feldspar and usually occurs as elongate crystals (Figure 70). Ferromagnesian minerals (purple and green in Figure 70) are slightly less abundant than feldspar.

Porphyritic gabbro commonly contains phenocrysts of labradorite plagioclase or pyroxene. The groundmass is finely crystalline but not aphanitic. Gabbro is not exceedingly common, but large exposures occur in Labrador and Finland.

29

Hand specimen

Figure 71. Obsidian.

Photomicrograph (X20)

Flow   Glass
lines

Hand specimen

Figure 72. Pumice.

Photomicrograph (X20)

"Glass threads"

Hand specimen

Figure 73. Tuff.

Photomicrograph (X20)

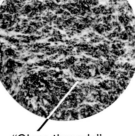

Pumice Crystal fragment

Volcanic Glass and Pyroclastics

OBSIDIAN. Obsidian is a massive volcanic glass. It breaks with a conchoidal fracture and has a bright, glassy luster (Figure 71). In spite of its composition, it is characteristically jet black due to the presence of countless dustlike particles of magnetite or ferromagnesian minerals. More rarely, yellow, red, or brown hues are produced by oxidized magnetite or hematite. In thin section (Figure 71), flow lines are expressed, but the rock appears totally black under polarized light. Although obsidian is not crystalline, it does contain skeletal crystal embryos called crystallites. Many aphanitic rocks contain appreciable quantities of glass filling interstices between crystals.

PUMICE. Pumice is a very porous volcanic glass. Its texture (both in hand specimen and thin section) consists of subparallel, silky glass fibers tangled together (Figure 72). It originates when relief of pressure in a volcano permits rapid expansion of gases through the upper part of the ascending column of obsidian lava. The lava swells into a froth or foam with innumerable minute bubbles and solidifies.

TUFF AND ASSOCIATED ROCKS. Fragmental material and droplets of lava expelled from volcanic vents and transported through the air are referred to as pyroclastics. Rocks formed from the consolidation of this material are classified according to grain size as follows: (1) Tuff (fine ash and dust less than one-fourth inch in diameter), (2) Volcanic Breccia (coarse ash and angular blocks one-fourth to two inches in diameter), and (3) Agglomerates (volcanic bombs and blocks greater than two inches in diameter).

The tuff illustrated in Figure 73 is composed of coarse fragments of pumice and fine ash. Common colors range from yellow through gray, pink, light brown, and dark grayish brown. Tuff is characteristically lightweight and poorly indurated. Volcanic breccia and agglomerate are commonly more dense and darker in color and contain fragments of pumice, obsidian, aphanitic rocks, and some fragments of the surrounding rock.

Pyroclastic material deposited on land is readily eroded, transported by water, and redeposited with other sedimentary material.

Photomicrograph (X20)

Figure 74. Peridotite.

Peridotite Family

The peridotite family is characterized by the following mineral composition:

Olivine 85-100%
Pyroxene........................... 0-10%
Ca Plagioclase.......................0-5%
Ore Minerals (magnetite,
ilmenite, chromite, etc.) 0-10%

PERIDOTITE. Peridotite is an easy rock to identify because it is composed almost entirely of the mineral olivine. The crystals of olivine are characteristically light green and have a distinctive glassy luster. They are typically equidimensional and are medium to coarse grained, so that in hand specimen a peridotite resembles a green, glassy sandstone. In the specimen shown in Figure 74, light glassy green crystals of olivine form the bulk of the rock, with the dark grains being pyroxene. This specimen is typical of peridotites extruded with basaltic magma and is believed to be part of the upper mantle carried as an inclusion in the lava and extruded as a volcanic bomb. The dark rim around the peridotite is basalt.

Rocks of the peridotite family all have phaneritic textures and originate far below the surface. No extrusive rocks with equivalent composition have been found.

Peridotites are not an abundant rock type in the earth's crust but they are very important in the study of the earth's dynamics because the entire upper mantle is composed almost exclusively of this type of rock. Indeed, the entire asthenosphere and lower lithosphere consist of peridotite, and it is this material which is moving to produce the earth's tectonic system. As the asthenosphere slowly moves in a convection cell, peridotite in the upward-moving currents is progressively subjected to less and less pressure and begins to melt. Plagioclase and pyroxene, having lower melting points than olivine, melt first and form a basaltic magma which is injected into the rift system to form new oceanic crust.

The Origin of Magma

The origin of magma is, of course, not known from direct observations, so our understanding of the chemistry and physics of liquid rocks is based on observations of volcanic products and synthetic magmas made in the laboratory, plus studies of geophysical properties of the earth, such as density, seismic properties, and regional structural features. Although much remains uncertain, we do have significant knowledge about the boundaries or limitations under which magma may be generated and about some aspects of the mechanism by which it is emplaced in the earth's crust.

We know from seismic evidence that the earth is solid down to a depth of 1800 miles and that only the outer core of the earth is liquid. The density of the liquid core, however, ranges from 9 to 10 gm/cm^3, which is far greater than any magma or igneous rocks in the crust (basalt has a density of 3). Thus, contrary to popular belief, it is very unlikely that magma comes from the liquid outer core of the earth, or even from the lower or central part of the mantle. Magma must originate from local melting of solid rock in the upper mantle and lower crust, at depths ranging only from 20 to 100 miles below the surface.

An important fact in considering the origin and composition of a magma is that each mineral in a rock has its own melting point; therefore, when a rock is heated, certain minerals will melt first, followed by others in a definite sequence. As a result, partial melting of a rock may produce a magma quite different in composition from the original rock. Two areas are of prime importance in the generation of magma: (1) the mid-oceanic ridge, where lithospheric plates are pulled apart, and (2) the subduction zone, where plates converge and one descends back into the mantle. In both areas, variations in temperature are produced by the moving plates and convecting mantle and produce partial melting.

In the mid-oceanic ridge (Figure 75) the upper mantle is believed to be rising as a result of convection in the asthenosphere. It is composed of peridotite, a rock made up almost exclusively of the minerals olivine, pyroxene, and minor amounts of plagioclase. As the rock is heated, plagioclase melts first, followed by pyroxene and ultimately olivine. Partial melting of peridotite would produce a magma richer in plagioclase and pyroxene—a basaltic magma. The extensive extrusions of basaltic magma along the mid-oceanic ridge and in the volcanoes of the ocean basins are considered to be magmas originating from partial melting of the upper mantle.

At the subduction zone the basaltic oceanic crust and veneer of sediments descend back into the mantle and are heated by the friction between moving plates together with the higher temperature at depth (Figure 75). Partial melting of the basaltic crust would produce a magma richer in silica (see Figure 55) which would rise upward in the orogenic belt to produce granitic intrusions and andesitic-rhyolitic flows. The extreme pressures in the roots of a deformed mountain belt at converging plate junctions would also increase the temperatures enough to begin melting some of the minerals in the metamorphic rocks. The liquid would rise upward, collect in larger bodies, and produce chambers of granitic magma.

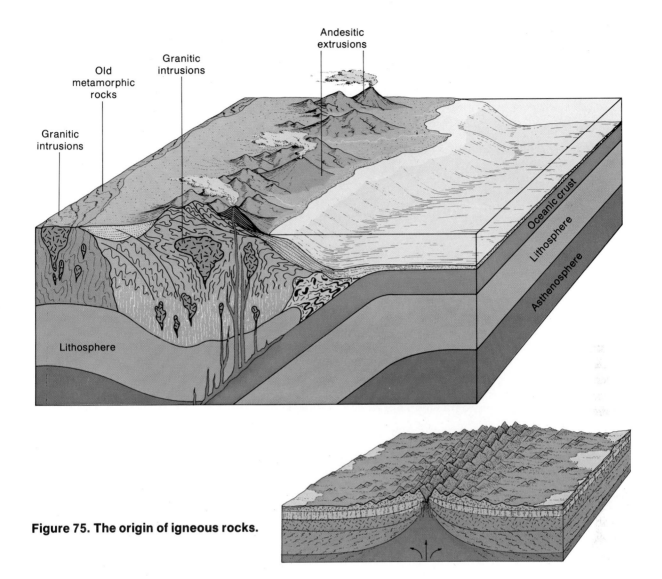

Figure 75. The origin of igneous rocks.

Problems

1. Identify the specimens provided by your instructor.

2. Compare your specimens with the illustrations and descriptions on pages 27 to 31. What are the distinguishing characteristics of each rock type? How does your specimen differ from the same rock type illustrated in this manual? Is this difference a fundamental difference in texture and composition or a minor difference in color, shape of specimen, etc.?

3. What geologic events are implied if a granite body is found exposed at the surface?

4. Which rock type would most likely form in a sill? In a laccolith? Why?

5. In Hawaii many basalt flows are only one to two feet thick. In the Columbia Plateau many are 20 to 40 feet thick. What factor is important in determining the thickness of basalt flows?

6. What minerals are likely to form phenocrysts in a basalt? Why?

7. Could phenocrysts be found in an obsidian? Briefly explain.

8. What are the major differences between a tuff and a quartz sandstone?

9. A granite may be pink, red, or various shades of gray and may be coarse, medium, or fine grained. What characteristics are found in all granites which serve to distinguish them from other rock types?

10. What is the difference between granite and diorite?

11. What is the origin of vesicles in a basalt?

12. What is the difference between basalt and andesite?

13. What rock type is most abundant in the crust of the ocean floors? What is the origin of magma in this area?

14. What igneous rock types form in a mountain belt? Why are these different from those forming at the mid-oceanic ridge?

4 Sedimentary Rocks

Sedimentary rocks are derived from erosional debris of other rocks and are deposited at the earth's surface at normal temperatures and pressures. The major processes involved in their genesis are: (1) physical and chemical weathering of the parent rock material; (2) transportation of the weathered products by running water, wind, gravity, or ice; (3) deposition of the material in a sedimentary basin; and (4) compaction and cementation of the sediment into a solid rock. These processes are in continual operation and are subject to man's observations.

One of the most significant results of transportation and deposition of sediment is the delicate mechanical and chemical sorting of the parent material referred to as *sedimentary differentiation.* Materials similar in size and weight accumulate in a specific sedimentary environment according to the level of mechanical energy operating at the time of deposition. Chemical sorting occurs contemporaneously as the more soluble materials are dissolved and removed in solution. For example, coarse gravels may be deposited in an alluvial fan near a mountain front or in a river bar, while the sand is transported downstream to be concentrated on a beach. Currents and wave action wash away the fine mud which is ultimately deposited in an environment of low mechanical energy, such as a marsh or a lagoon. Calcium carbonate will generally be dissolved during this process and be precipitated in shallow water free from sand and mud. If sedimentary processes operate over a long period, sedimentary differentiation will reach a remarkable degree of perfection.

Composition

Inasmuch as sediment is derived from any preexisting source rock, one might expect the composition of sedimentary rocks to be extremely variable and complex. This is indeed true if the sediment is deposited close to the source area; but if weathering and erosion are prolonged, sedimentary differentiation will concentrate materials similar in size, shape, and composition in separate deposits. *Most sedimentary rocks are thus composed of materials which are abundant in other rocks and are stable under surface temperature and pressure. The great bulk of most sedimentary rocks is composed of only four constituents: (1) quartz, (2) calcite, (3) clay, and (4) rock fragments.*

Quartz. Quartz is the most abundant clastic mineral in sedimentary rocks. The reason for this is readily apparent, for quartz is one of the most abundant minerals in the granitic continental crust and it is extremely hard, resistant, and chemically stable. Sedimentary processes will decompose and disintegrate less stable minerals and concentrate quartz as deposits of sand. Silica in solution or in particles of colloidal size is also a product of weathering of igneous rocks and is commonly precipitated as a cement in certain coarse-grained sediments.

Calcite. Calcite is the major constituent of limestone and is the most common cementing material in sands and shales. Calcium is derived from igneous rocks rich in calcium-bearing minerals such as calcic plagioclase. The carbonate is derived from water and carbon dioxide. Calcium is precipitated as $CaCO_3$ or is extracted from sea water by organisms and concentrated as shell material. When the organisms die, the shell and shell fragments commonly accumulate as clastic particles which ultimately form a variety of limestone.

Clay. Clay minerals develop from the weathering of silicates, particularly the feldspars. They are very fine grained and are concentrated in mud and shale. The abundance of feldspar in the earth's crust, together with the fact that it readily decomposes under atmospheric conditions, accounts for the large amount of clay minerals in sedimentary rocks.

Rock Fragments. Fragments of the parent rock in which the constituent minerals are not disaggregated are the major constituents of coarse-grained clastic rocks. Rock fragments are most abundant in deposits of gravel, but some sandstones are composed predominantly of basalt, slate, or some other fine-grained rocks.

Other Minerals in Sedimentary Rocks. Deposits of quartz, calcite, and clay, either alone or in various combinations, represent the great bulk of sedimentary rocks, but certain other minerals are abundant enough to form distinct strata. *Dolomite*, $CaMg(CO_3)_2$, may replace calcite in limestone. *Feldspars* and *mica* may be concentrated in some sandstones if weathering, erosion, and deposition are rapid. *Halite* and *gypsum* are precipitated by evaporation of sea water and in certain environments may accumulate in thick layers. *Organic matter* is generally rare in sedimentary rocks, but accumulations of plant material may become thick beds of coal.

Sedimentary Structures

A number of structures are unique to sedimentary rocks and are important identifying features of this rock class. The most significant are the various types of stratification, or layering, produced by physical or chemical changes that occur during transportation and during deposition within the sedimentary environment. Layers may range from a fraction of an inch to many feet in thickness. Inasmuch as sediments accumulate by vertical and lateral accretion, two basic types of layers result: (1) horizontal layers and (2) cross-bedding. Cross-bedding is of particular significance in that it indicates the direction in which the depositing currents were moving.

Ripple marks, mud cracks, and rain imprints are familiar to anyone who has walked along a seashore or by a stream. These features, commonly preserved in sedimentary rock, are important indicators of environments.

Textures

Textures in sedimentary rocks are significant in that they provide important clues concerning distance of transportation and environments of deposition. Two basically different types of textures are recognized: (1) clastic textures (fragments of rock debris) and (2) crystalline textures (crystals which have grown from solutions).

Clastic Textures. (Figures 76 and 77) The basic criterion for classifying clastic textures is *grain size*, with subordinate subdivisions made on the basis of *rounding*, *sorting*, and *cementation*. The size of clastic particles ranges from large blocks, many feet in diameter, to fine dust. Particles are referred to as coarse grained (over 2 mm in diameter), medium grained (1/16 to 2 mm in diameter), and fine grained (less than 1/16 mm in diameter).

Rock fragments and mineral particles may be rounded (Figure 76A), subangular (Figure 76C), or angular (Figure 76B), depending upon the amount of abrasion they have been subjected to. Sediment moved by ice or the direct action of gravity is commonly very angular, whereas particles carried by wind and water are rounded by abrasion. In a general way, grain size and rounding are a rough measure of distance over which the particles have been transported. Large, angular boulders indicate a nearby source because any significant transport by streams would rapidly round off the corners and wear down the size.

Sorting refers to the range of various sizes of particles. It is a very important textural characteristic since it may provide clues concerning the history of transportation and the environment in which the sediment accumulated. Well-sorted material (Figure 77) is composed of one dominant size and usually one type of material. It results only after considerable transportation, during which particles similar in size and density are concentrated by prolonged washing and winnowing by current action. Poorly sorted material (Figure 76A) contains several different sizes. Glaciers do not sort materials but deposit coarse and fine particles together. Mudflows do the same. Wind and water are the best sorting agents; they usually concentrate materials of one dominant grain size in dunes, beaches, bars, and mud flats.

After a sediment is deposited, it may become tightly cemented together to form a solid rock. The dominant cementing materials are calcite, quartz, iron, and chert, which may be carried by ground water from a foreign source or derived within or very near the site of sedimentation by solution activity. The degree to which a sediment is cemented is thus an important textural characteristic in clastic rocks.

Crystalline Textures. (Figures 78 and 79) In contrast to the clastic texture described above, minerals precipitated from sea water or lakes develop a texture consisting of a network of interlocking crystals. Such textures are similar to those found in igneous rocks but generally consist of one dominant mineral. The individual crystals are usually about the same size and interlock to form a dense rock. Crystalline textures are described as coarse (greater than 2 mm), medium (1/16 mm to 2 mm, Figure 78A), and fine or microcrystalline (less than 1/16 mm, Figure 78B). Deposits from springs and caves are commonly microcrystalline but have a banded structure (Figure 78C) resulting from chemical variations and impurities during deposition.

Oolitic Texture. Calcium carbonate precipitated on a sea floor and agitated by wave or current action commonly accumulates around a tiny shell fragment or grain of silt. As the particle moves to and fro, small spheres called oolites are built up by accretion and form a limestone texture which superficially resembles a well-rounded sandstone. Close examination of an oolitic texture reveals a concentric structure around a nucleus and generally minor amounts of associated shell debris (Figure 88C).

Skeletal Textures. Calcium carbonate may also be removed from sea water by organisms to make their shells and other hard parts. When the organisms die, the shell material will settle to the sea floor and may be concentrated as shell fragments on a beach or near a reef. The texture of the resulting rock is similar to a clastic texture, but the material is unique in that it consists of the skeletal fragments of organisms. Such a texture is referred to as skeletal (Figures 79A and B) and is of fundamental importance in many limestones.

Clastic Textures

A   B   C

Figure 76. Examples of clastic textures (actual size).

The samples shown above illustrate a variety of coarse clastic textures. All are composed of fragments greater than 2 mm in diameter. In Specimen A, large rounded pebbles composed mostly of quartzite are surrounded by a matrix of red sand and silt. The material is poorly sorted but a crude stratification is present. In Specimen B, two grain sizes are preserved—a fine sand-size matrix and coarse-grained pebbles. The angularity of the pebbles is an important textural characteristic of this rock and serves to distinguish it from the other coarse-grained sediments. In Specimen C, the grains are moderately well sorted and subangular and represent the border line between a medium- and coarse-grained texture.

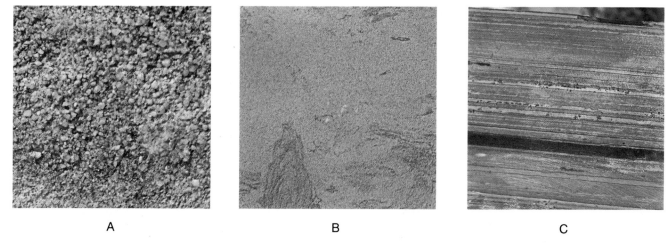

A   B   C

Figure 77. Examples of medium- to fine-grained clastic textures (actual size).

Specimen A is typical of a medium-grained clastic texture. The grains are less than 2 mm and are well rounded and well sorted. A fine-grained clastic texture is shown in Specimen B. Individual grains are too small to be distinguished with the unaided eye but are well sorted. A microscopic view of this texture is shown in Figure 84. Redistribution of these silt-sized particles by burrowing organisms is common and is evident in the lower left corner of the photo.

The finest-grained clastic texture is illustrated in C. Individual particles are less than 1/256 mm and cannot be seen without high magnification. Lamination like that shown in C is common in fine-grained clastic rocks. (See photomicrograph of this texture in Figure 85.)

Textures of Limestones

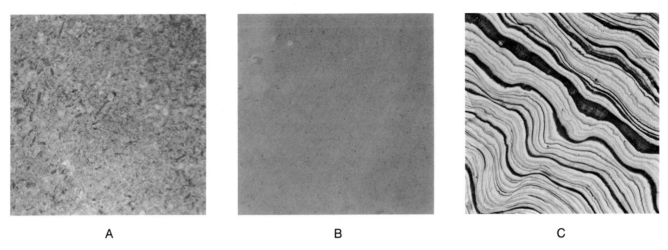

A   B   C

Figure 78. Examples of limestone textures (actual size).

Calcium carbonate precipitated from the sea or lakes may form a texture of interlocking crystal. The crystal size ranges from large crystals greater than one inch long to small submicroscopic grains. In Specimen A, the texture is coarse, crystalline, and equigranular. Microcrystalline material, such as shown in B, forms a very dense, structureless rock. Even under the microscope the crystal material is difficult to distinguish. With extremely high magnification, discrete crystals can be identified. Some microcrystalline material is characteristically banded due to variations in conditions during deposition, such as illustrated by Specimen C.

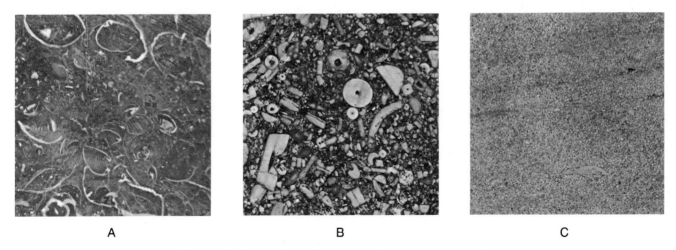

A   B   C

Figure 79. Examples of limestone textures (actual size).

Organisms play an important role in many limestone textures. Shells and shell fragments accumulate after the organisms die and may dominate the textural aspect of the rock. In Specimen A, cross sections of shells of clamlike organisms are shown in white. Crinoid stem fragments are shown in Specimen B. Oolitic textures, such as are shown in Specimen C, develop when a silt particle or shell fragment is shifted to and fro by waves and picks up newly precipitated calcium carbonate. A microscopic view of oolites is shown in Figure 88.

Classification of Sedimentary Rocks

Sedimentary differentiation provides a logical basis for classification, but the wide variety of source material and sedimentary environments makes it difficult to formulate a scheme of classification which will encompass all rock types. Clastic rocks, for example, result from processes distinctly different from those which develop chemical precipitates and organic sediments. It is thus convenient to recognize two major classes of sedimentary rocks: (1) clastic and (2) chemical-organic. Further subdivision is made in each group on the basis of texture, composition, and other significant properties. Many different kinds of sedimentary rocks have been described, but over 95 percent of the total volume of sediment is made up of varieties of sandstone, limestone, or shale.

Clastic rocks are classified according to grain size, with subsequent subdivision based on composition. The size range, compositional types, and nomenclature are shown in Table 5A.

Chemical precipitates are classified on the basis of composition, with subdivisions based on texture or other outstanding features as shown in Table 5B.

TABLE 5. CLASSIFICATION OF SEDIMENTARY ROCKS
A. CLASTIC ROCKS

Texture	Composition	Rock Name
COARSE GRAINED (over 2 mm)	Rounded fragments of any rock type—quartz, quartzite, chert dominant	CONGLOMERATE
COARSE GRAINED (over 2 mm)	Angular fragments of any rock type—quartz, quartzite, chert dominant	BRECCIA
MEDIUM GRAINED (1/16 mm to 2 mm)	Quartz with minor accessory minerals	QUARTZ SANDSTONE
MEDIUM GRAINED (1/16 mm to 2 mm)	Quartz with at least 25% feldspar	ARKOSE
MEDIUM GRAINED (1/16 mm to 2 mm)	Quartz, rock fragments, and considerable clay	GRAYWACKE
FINE GRAINED (1/256 to 1/16 mm)	Quartz and clay minerals	SILTSTONE
VERY FINE GRAINED (less than 1/256 mm)	Quartz and clay minerals	SHALE

B. CHEMICAL PRECIPITATES

Texture	Composition	Rock Name
Medium to coarse grained	CALCITE ($CaCO_3$)	CRYSTALLINE LIMESTONE
Microcrystalline, conchoidal fracture	CALCITE ($CaCO_3$)	MICRITE
Aggregates of oolites	CALCITE ($CaCO_3$)	OOLITIC LIMESTONE
Fossils and fossil fragments loosely cemented	CALCITE ($CaCO_3$)	COQUINA
Abundant fossils in calcareous matrix	CALCITE ($CaCO_3$)	FOSSILIFEROUS LIMESTONE
Shells of microscopic organisms, clay—soft	CALCITE ($CaCO_3$)	CHALK
Banded calcite	CALCITE ($CaCO_3$)	TRAVERTINE
Textures are similar to those in limestone	DOLOMITE $CaMg(CO_3)_2$	DOLOMITE
Cryptocrystalline, dense	CHALCEDONY (SiO_2)	CHERT, ETC.
Fine to coarse crystalline	GYPSUM ($CaSO_4 \cdot 2H_2O$)	GYPSUM
Fine to coarse crystalline	HALITE ($NaCl$)	ROCK SALT

Figure 80. Conglomerate.

Photomicrograph (X20)

Quartz   Sand
pebble   matrix

Hand specimen

Figure 81. Breccia.

Photomicrograph (X20)

Angular rock
fragments

Hand specimen

Figure 82. Arkose.

Photomicrograph (X20)

Feldspar   Quartz

Clastic Rocks

Clastic rocks consist predominantly of fragments and debris of other rock material. These deposits are familiar as gravel, sand, and mud when unconsolidated and are referred to as conglomerate, sandstone, and shale when indurated. Most of the material in the sedimentary record is sorted and stratified, and shows the effects of abrasion. Classification of clastic rocks is made on the basis of texture and composition.

CONGLOMERATE. Conglomerates consist of coarse rock fragments (greater than 2 mm in diameter), held together by a matrix of sand, clay, and cement. The individual pebbles are usually well rounded and moderately well sorted (Figure 80). Pebbles in conglomerates may consist of any mineral or rock, but resistant materials such as quartz, quartzite, and chert are especially common. Fragments of limestone, granite, or other rock types may predominate in some deposits.

The only agents capable of transporting gravels and large fragments are swift-moving water, ice, and gravity. The most important environments for conglomerate deposition are alluvial fans, river channels, and beaches.

BRECCIA. A breccia is a coarse-grained clastic rock in which the fragments are angular and show little evidence of abrasion (Figure 81). The material is commonly poorly sorted, with a fine-grained matrix.

The most significant breccia deposits result from glaciation, landslides, and other types of mass movement. Movement along fault planes will also produce a breccia zone, as will collapse in caves.

ARKOSES. An arkose (Figure 82) is a clastic rock which is composed of at least 25 percent feldspar. Quartz is the other major constituent. Arkose is generally coarse grained, angular, and moderately well sorted. In most arkoses the grain size is commonly in the sand range, but some arkoses are coarse enough to be termed conglomerates. In Figure 82, the feldspar is pink, and close inspection will reveal that it is very abundant. In thin section the feldspar grains, which have a plaid pattern, are nearly as abundant as quartz (gray). Calcite cement appears brown in the thin section.

Arkoses form by rapid erosion of a granitic terrain and rapid deposition. They are common in alluvial fans.

Hand specimen

Figure 83. Quartz sandstone.

Photomicrograph (X20)

Quartz

SANDSTONES. Sandstones are clastic sedimentary rocks consisting mostly of grains ranging from 1/16 to 2 mm in diameter. The grains are generally rounded and show other effects of abrasion (thin section, Figure 83). Quartz is usually the dominant mineral, although feldspar, garnet, mica, and other minerals may be present in varying amounts. Poorly sorted, dirty sandstones containing over 20 percent clay are called *graywacke.* Calcite, quartz, and iron oxide are the dominant cementing materials. Sandstones are generally stratified and are colored buff, red, brown, yellow, or green, depending on impurities and cementing agents.

Sandstones may accumulate in a wide variety of environments, such as beaches, deserts, flood plains, and deltas.

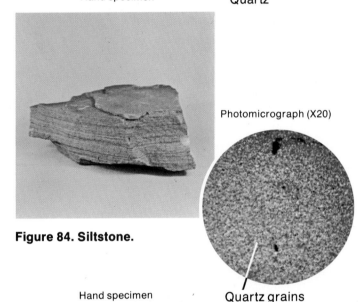

Hand specimen

Figure 84. Siltstone.

Photomicrograph (X20)

Quartz grains

SILTSTONES. Siltstones are fine-grained clastic rocks in which at least 50 percent of the material is 1/16 to 1/256 mm in diameter. They are commonly laminated (Figure 84), but burrowing organisms may destroy or obscure evidences of stratification. Silt particles, when viewed under the microscope, appear to be angular rather than rounded like sand. They are composed of quartz grains, with an abundance of mica and clay minerals.

Silt is a common material deposited by most streams in deltas and flood plains. It rarely forms thick beds and is characteristically interstratified with shales and sandstones.

Hand specimen

Figure 85. Shale.

Photomicrograph (X20)

Clay minerals   Laminae

SHALES. Shales (Figure 85) are fine-grained clastic rocks consisting of particles less than 1/256 mm in diameter. They are characteristically laminated or thin bedded, as is well expressed in both hand specimen and thin section. Quartz, mica, and the clay minerals are the dominant constituents, but, as is shown in Figure 85, the particles are too small to be seen without a high magnification. Calcite may be present—usually as a cement—in amounts ranging up to 50 percent.

Eighty percent of exposed sedimentary rocks are shales. They accumulate in an environment of low mechanical energy such as lagoons, quiet offshore waters, flood plains, and lakes.

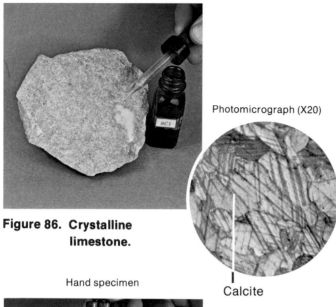

Figure 86. Crystalline limestone.

Photomicrograph (X20)

Calcite

Hand specimen

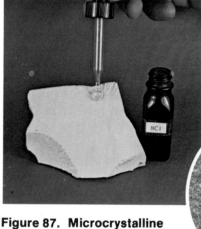

Figure 87. Microcrystalline limestone.

Photomicrograph (X20)

Microcrystalline calcite

Hand specimen

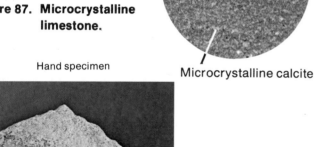

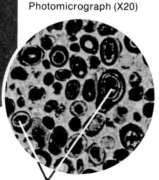

Figure 88. Oolitic limestone.

Photomicrograph (X20)

Oolites

Limestone

Limestones are sedimentary rocks that contain more than 50 percent calcium carbonate. Impurities, which may range in amount to 50 percent, include clay, quartz, iron oxide, rock fragments, and other material. The calcite may be precipitated chemically or organically or may be of detrital origin. The many varieties of limestones are classified on the basis of texture or some other significant property. All limestones are similar in that they are composed mostly of calcite and effervesce in hydrochloric acid.

CRYSTALLINE LIMESTONE (Sparite). Crystalline limestone (Figure 86) is composed of interlocking crystals of calcite which can be seen with the unaided eye or with low-power magnification. In many respects it is similar to a marble, but it shows no evidence of pressure or flowage. Well-preserved fossils are common, and bedding planes are generally distinct. Good rhombohedral cleavage is commonly well expressed in thin sections of crystalline limestone.

Large crystals in limestone may grow after deposition if ground-water solutions migrate through the rock and precipitate calcite.

MICROCRYSTALLINE LIMESTONE (Micrite). Microcrystalline limestone (Figure 87) is composed almost entirely of microscopic crystals of calcite so small that they are difficult to discriminate even under the microscope. The rock has uniform texture, is very dense, and characteristically breaks with a conchoidal fracture. It is commonly buff or light yellow but may range in color to dark gray or black if organic material is abundant.

Microcrystalline limestone forms in warm, quiet, shallow seas.

OOLITIC LIMESTONE. Oolitic limestone (Figure 88) is composed of small spheres of calcite concretions called oolites. The grains range up to 2 mm in diameter and consist of a sequence of concentric layers built around a nucleus of fine silt, clay, or shell fragments. Calcite commonly cements the oolites together into a rock which closely resembles a well-rounded quartz sandstone. Stratification, sorting, cross-bedding, and other features characteristic of a sandstone are also common in oolitic limestone.

Oolites originate in shallow water where the nucleus, agitated by currents and waves, rolls along the bottom and picks up calcite that adheres to its surface.

Hand specimen

Figure 89. Coquina.

Photomicrograph (X20)

Shell fragments

Hand specimen

Figure 90. Fossiliferous limestone.

Photomicrograph (X20)

Shell fragments

Hand specimen

Figure 91. Chalk.

Photomicrograph (X20)

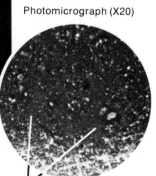

Clay and microscopic shells

COQUINA. Coquina (Figure 89) is the name given to a weak, porous, poorly cemented limestone composed almost exclusively of shells and shell fragments. The shell material in a coquina is commonly broken into platy fragments which are rounded, abraded, and well sorted, as is shown in the thin section.

Coquina is thus a particular type of clastic rock in which the fragmental material originated *within* the sedimentary environment rather than being transported to it from an eroded landmass. Coquinas are forming today along the southern Atlantic coast and in the Bahama Islands where shell material is washed up on the shore and accumulates as calcareous sand on a beach or in shallow marine water.

SKELETAL OR FOSSILIFEROUS LIMESTONE. Skeletal limestone (Figure 90) is composed primarily of hard parts of invertebrate organisms such as mollusks, corals, crinoids, and other invertebrates. This material is commonly cemented with calcite and forms a dense rock. Fossils may weather out in relief, however, and reveal minute details of rock textures. In thin section, details of fossil shell structure are clearly expressed.

Fossiliferous limestone forms in warm, shallow seas where marine life is abundant.

CHALK. Chalk is a soft, porous, fine-textured limestone composed of shells of microscopic organisms, mostly foraminifera. It is normally white or buff and may contain varying amounts of mud (Figure 91).

The best-known chalks are of Cretaceous age, such as the famous white chalk cliffs on both sides of the English Channel, the Selma Chalk of the Gulf coast, and the Niobrara Chalk of Kansas. Chalk is considered to be a shallow water deposit formed by the accumulation of shells of floating organisms.

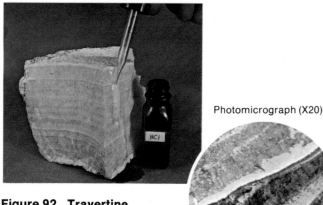

Hand specimen

Photomicrograph (X20)

Figure 92. Travertine.

Calcite

TRAVERTINE. Travertine (Figure 92) is a calcium carbonate deposit formed in caves and springs. It is characteristically banded with alternating light and dark layers resulting from minor amounts of iron oxide which accumulate during successive periods of deposition. The well-known flowstone, dripstone, stalagmites, and stalactites of caves are all varieties of travertine. Inasmuch as travertine forms relatively small deposits, mostly recent in age, it is of no great geologic importance, but it is of interest because of its beauty and the variety of forms in which it may occur.

Hand specimen

Photomicrograph (X20)

Figure 93. Gypsum.

Small gypsum crystals

ROCK GYPSUM. Rock gypsum is a chemical precipitate composed almost exclusively of aggregates of the mineral gypsum (Figure 93). It is normally white or is delicately colored in various shades of yellow or light red. One of its most distinctive characteristics is that it can be scratched with the fingernail. Gypsum is commonly massive, but thin, delicate laminae formed by seasonal influxes of clay are found in some deposits.

Gypsum originates from evaporation of saline lakes or sea water in restricted bays and thus indicates an arid or semiarid climate at the time of formation.

Hand specimen

Photomicrograph (X20)

Figure 94. Rock salt.

Halite crystals

ROCK SALT. Rock salt is a rock composed of the mineral halite. Crystals may be fine, medium, or coarse and are generally colorless, unless modified with impurities of iron oxide or clay to various shades of red (Figure 94).

The origin of rock salt is similar to that of gypsum. Thick salt deposits are found in Michigan, New York, and Kansas and in relatively recent deposits of the western states. One of the interesting and important characteristics of salt is that it flows at relatively low temperatures and pressures. Salt from deeply buried strata may rise as piercement plugs or salt domes.

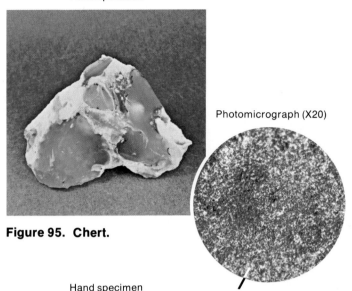

Figure 95. Chert.

Photomicrograph (X20)

Cryptocrystalline quartz

CHERT AND FLINT. Chert and flint (Figure 95) are common chemical siliceous sediments. The color may be white or various shades of gray, green, blue, red, yellow, or black. Under high magnification, they have a fibrous or granular texture. Chert and flint commonly occur as nodules in limestone and may be coated white. Like other varieties of quartz, chert and flint are characterized by a hardness of 7 and a conchoidal fracture.

A large amount of chert is deposited in limestones by ground water but some appears to be deposited in shallow seas with limestone.

Hand specimen

Figure 96. Peat.

Organic matter

PEAT. Peat is a dark brown or black residuum produced by partial decomposition and disintegration of plants (Figure 96). It represents the initial step in the formation of coal and forms in bogs and swamps. The organic residues constitute from 70 to 90 percent of the total accumulation. Mineral compounds are insignificant. The development of peat requires rapid growth and reproduction of plants and a minimum of life activity of microorganisms. Peat deposits may be tens of feet thick and cover many square miles.

Hand specimen

Figure 97. Coal.

Photomicrograph (X20)

Vitrain (red) Spores and resins (yellow) Fusain (black)

COAL. Coal (Figure 97) is composed of highly altered plant remains and various amounts of clay. It is opaque and noncrystalline, with colors ranging from light brown to black. Coalification results from the burial of peat and is classified according to the degree of change. Prolonged heat and pressure produce lignite (brown coal), bituminous (soft) coal, and anthracite (hard) coal.

The Origin of Sedimentary Rocks

The various types of sedimentary rocks described in this manual may be formed in a number of sedimentary environments. The term "sedimentary environment" refers to the place where the sediment is deposited and to the physical, chemical, and biological conditions which exist in that place. The diagram in Figure 98 shows in a general way the regional setting of some of the major environments, and the following brief summary outlines some of the important characteristics of the sedimentary rocks which form in each environment.

Alluvial Fans. Alluvial fans are deposits of sediment in a dry basin. They typically contain coarse boulders and gravels and are poorly sorted. Fine-grained sand and silt may be deposited near the margin of the fan out in the valley.

Flood Plains. The great rivers of the world commonly meander across a flat flood plain before reaching the sea and depositing a considerable amount of sediment. Rocks formed in a flood plain environment are commonly lenses of sandstone deposited in the meander channel enclosed in a shale deposited on the flood plain.

Eolian. Wind is an effective sorting agent and will selectively transport sand. Gravel is left behind and dust-sized particles are lifted high into the atmosphere and transported thousands of miles before accumulating as a thin blanket of loess. Windblown sand accumulates in dunes and is characterized by fine grains which are well sorted and by large-scale cross-bedding.

Glacial. Glaciers do not effectively sort the material they transport, so the resulting deposit is an unstratified accumulation of boulders, gravel, sand, and fine silt.

Delta. Deltas are large accumulations of sediment which are deposited at the mouth of a river. They are one of the most significant environments of sedimentation and include a number of subenvironments such as stream channels, flood plain beaches, bars, and tidal flats. The deposit as a whole consists of a thick accumulation of silt, mud, and sand.

Shoreline. Beaches, bars, and spits commonly develop along low coasts and partly enclose quiet-water lagoons. The sediment in the beaches and bars is well washed by wave action and is typically clean, well-sorted quartz sand. Behind the bars and adjacent to the beaches, tidal flats may occur where fine silt and mud are deposited.

Organic Reef. An organic reef is a solid structure of shells and secretions of marine organisms. The framework is typically built by corals and algae but many types of organisms contribute to the reef community. These organisms produce a highly fossiliferous limestone.

Shallow Marine. Shallow seas are widespread along the margins of the continents and in the past were even more extensive. Sediments deposited in these shallow marine waters form extensive layers of well-sorted sand, shale, and limestone, which typically occur in a cyclic sequence as a result of shifting environments from changes in sea level.

Deep Ocean. The deep ocean adjacent to the continents receives a considerable amount of sediment transported from the continental margins by turbidity currents. As the current moves across the deep-ocean floor its velocity gradually decreases and sediment carried in suspension settles out. The resulting deposit is a widespread layer of sediment in which the size of grains grade from coarse at the base to fine at the top. The deep-sea deposits are characterized by a sequence of graded beds.

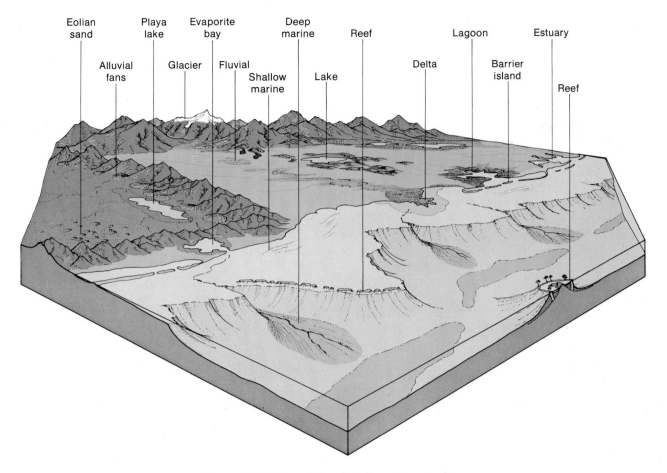

Figure 98. The origin of sedimentary rocks.

Problems

1. Identify the specimens provided by your instructor. To do this effectively, you should proceed as follows:

    a. Determine whether the rock is composed of calcium carbonate or not. (Rocks composed mostly of $CaCO_3$ will effervesce in dilute HCl; other rocks will not.)

    b. Determine whether the rock has a clastic (fragmental) or a crystalline texture. Use a hand lens or a microscope if one is available.

    c. Determine the grain size and matrix.
    Clastic—Decide whether the grains are dominantly gravel, sand, silt, or clay size. Note the abundance of matrix material.
    Crystalline carbonates—Decide whether the texture is coarse, medium, or fine crystalline.
    Clastic carbonates—Decide whether the texture is predominantly oolitic or fossiliferous.

    d. Determine the composition of the matrix.

    e. With the above information, refer to Table 5 and determine the rock name.

2. Compare your specimen with the illustrations and descriptions on pages 42 to 47. How does your specimen differ from the illustration of the same rock type? Are the differences of fundamental importance (e.g., differences of composition or texture) or are they minor (e.g., a difference in color)?

3. What geologic events are indicated by a clean, well-sorted quartz sandstone?

4. How would these events differ in the formation of an arkose?

5. List the environments in which shale accumulates. What does each of these have in common with the others?

6. Many limestones have a crystalline texture. What features of a limestone indicate that it is not igneous?

7. What evidence indicates that sandstone forms at the earth's surface and not at great depth?

8. What are the major processes involved in the genesis of sedimentary rocks?

9. How is $CaCO_3$ extracted from sea water?

10. What is the origin of clay minerals?

11. What rock types occur as fragments in sandstone?

12. Why is olivine a rare mineral in sandstone—even on the beaches of volcanic islands?

13. What properties are common to all limestones regardless of texture?

14. Many limestones are dense, fine grained, and black. How can you distinguish between a limestone and a basalt?

15. How do oolites originate? Where are they deposited?

16. Where do coquinas form?

17. How are rock salt and rock gypsum formed?

18. What is an arkose? How does it differ from a quartz sandstone?

19. What is the major source rock of an arkose?

20. Study the environments shown in Figure 98 and list the rock types likely to be formed in each major environment.

21. Why can sandstone be formed in so many different environments?

5 Metamorphic Rocks

Metamorphic rocks are those which have been fundamentally changed by heat, pressure, and the chemical action of fluids and gases. The parent material may include marine sediments which formed at surface temperature and pressure, interbedded with lava which crystallized at high temperatures and granite which subsequently intruded the entire sequence. These materials would be unstable at temperatures and pressures prevailing in the interior of the crust, especially an orogenic belt where plates of the lithosphere collide. The rocks thus react in such a way as to produce a new assemblage of minerals stable under the new conditions. Metamorphic changes are always in a direction which tends to restore equilibrium. The effects of metamorphism include: (1) chemical recombination and growth of new minerals, with or without the addition of new elements from circulating fluids and gases, (2) deformation and rotation of the constituent mineral grains, and (3) recrystallization of minerals into larger grains. The net result is a rock of greater crystallinity and hardness, possessing new structural features which commonly exhibit flowage or other expressions of deformation. All three major rock types may be metamorphosed, but intrusive igneous rocks and previously metamorphosed rocks which originate in an environment of high temperature and pressure are less affected than sedimentary rocks which develop on the earth's surface.

Types of Metamorphism

Contact Metamorphism

Contact metamorphism results from high temperatures and a vigorous solution activity concentrated near the contacts of cooling magma. This type of metamorphism is of a local nature and rapidly diminishes away from the intrusive body. Heat and chemical activity are the major agents, and the rocks affected generally recrystallize into hard, massive bodies. If escaping vapors and solutions add material to the surrounding rock, new minerals result, and parts of the original rock may be completely replaced.

Regional Metamorphism

Regional metamorphism results from the combined action of high temperatures and directed stresses. It is common where plates of the lithosphere collide. The rocks are characteristically folded into mountain belts, crushed, sheared, and stretched. Rocks in the roots of orogenic belts are generally altered by this type of metamorphism.

Careful field and laboratory studies indicate that certain mineral assemblages are indicative of various degrees of metamorphism. Chlorite, talc, and micas form by mild metamorphism, whereas garnet and amphibole develop under more intense conditions.

Foliation

Foliation is a planar element in metamorphic rocks. It may be expressed by closely spaced fractures *(slaty cleavage)*, by parallel arrangement of platy minerals *(schistosity)*, or by alternating layers of differing mineralogic composition *(gneissic layering)*, some of which may be

Foliated Textures

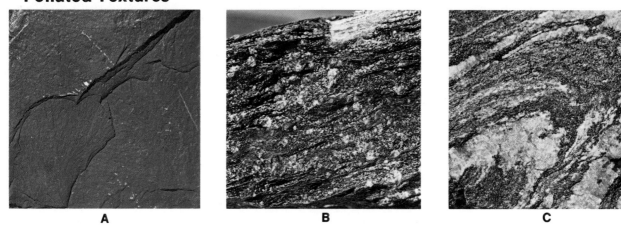

Figure 99. Examples of foliated textures (actual size).

Slaty cleavage (Specimen A) is a type of foliation expressed by the tendency of a rock to split along subparallel planes. It should not be confused with bedding planes, for it may cut across relic bedding at a high angle. Slaty cleavage results from parallel orientation of microscopic platy minerals such as mica, talc, or chlorite. These minerals grow in a metamorphic environment, with their flat surfaces perpendicular to the applied forces. The perfect cleavage within the minerals creates a definite zone of weakness, allowing the rock to break along nearly parallel planes such as the surfaces shown in Specimen A.

A higher grade of metamorphism produces a greater textural adjustment. Mica, chlorite, and talc grow into visible crystals and develop a type of foliation known as schistosity (Specimen B). Schistosity is thus similar in character to slaty cleavage, but the platy minerals are much larger, and the entire rock appears to be coarse grained. The increase in crystal size represents a higher grade of metamorphism in which garnet, amphibole, and other nonplaty minerals develop. Schistosity typically develops in mica-rich rocks.

Specimen C illustrates an example of gneissic layering, a type of foliation in which the planar element is produced by *alternating layers of different mineralogical composition.* Rocks containing gneissic layering are characteristically coarse grained and represent a higher grade of metamorphism in which the minerals are stretched, mashed, and completely rearranged. Feldspars and quartz commonly form light-colored layers which alternate with dark layers of ferromagnesian minerals.

Nonfoliated Textures

Figure 100. Examples of nonfoliated textures (actual size).

In some metamorphic rocks, little or no foliation develops, and the rock appears to be structureless except for evidences of deformation of constituent mineral grains. A metamorphosed conglomerate, such as that shown in Specimen A, will commonly show elongated pebbles which have been stretched in response to directional forces. Sand grains in a metamorphic sandstone will commonly show a similar expression of deformation, or the grains may be fused together in a dense, compact mass of interlocking particles (Specimen B). Deformation of limestone will produce stretches or streaks of organic debris (Specimen C).

relic stratification. Foliation is usually developed during metamorphism by directed stresses which cause differential movement or recrystallization. It constitutes a fundamental characteristic of metamorphic rocks and is a basic criterion in their classification. An illustration of the various types of foliation is shown in Figure 99.

Some metamorphic rocks do not possess a foliation but appear structureless except for elongate grains or other linear features resulting from directional stresses. Nonfoliated rocks are commonly composed of only one mineral. Structural types are illustrated in Figure 100.

Classification of Metamorphic Rocks

Metamorphic rocks are highly complex, and it is difficult to formulate a satisfactory classification based on mineralogy or mode or origin. The most convenient scheme of classification is to group metamorphic rocks according to structural features, with further subdivision based on composition. With this classification, two major groups of metamorphic rocks are recognized: (1) those which are foliated (possess a definite planar structure) and (2) those which are not foliated but are massive and structureless. The foliated rocks may be further subdivided according to the type of foliation. A large variety of rock types may subsequently be recognized in each group according to the dominant minerals. The basic framework of this classification is shown in Table 6.

TABLE 6. CLASSIFICATION OF METAMORPHIC ROCKS

A. FOLIATED

Texture			Composition						Rock Name
Oriented Grains	NONLAYERED	Very Fine Grained	CHLORITE	MICA	QUARTZ	FELDSPAR	AMPHIBOLE	PYROXENE	SLATE
		Fine Grained							PHYLLITE
		Coarse Grained							SCHIST
	LAYERED	Coarse Grained							GNEISS

B. NONFOLIATED

Texture	Composition	Rock Name
Coarse Grained	Deformed Fragments of Any Rock Type	METACONGLOMERATE
Fine to Coarse Grained	Quartz	QUARTZITE
	Calcite or Dolomite	MARBLE

Foliated Rocks

SLATES. Slates are fine-grained metamorphic rocks possessing a type of foliation known as slaty cleavage, the horizontal planar element shown in Figure 101. In many slates, traces of original bedding are expressed by changes in color or grain size and are commonly at an angle to the foliation (light bands in Figure 101). Common minerals are quartz, muscovite, and chlorite, but crystals are generally so small that they can be seen only under high magnification. Slates are characteristically dense and brittle and are colored gray, black, red, or green. They are low-rank metamorphic rocks derived principally from shales.

Hand specimen

Figure 101. Slate.

Photomicrograph (X20)

Deformed shale particles

PHYLLITES. Phyllites (Figure 102) are similar to slates but are distinguished from them by a satinlike luster or sheen developed on the planes of foliation. In thin section, phyllites display a slightly coarser grain size than slates. Compare thin section of Figure 101 with Figure 102.

Hand specimen

Figure 102. Phyllite.

Photomicrograph (X20)

Mica crystals

SCHISTS. Schists (Figures 103 and 104) are metamorphic rocks in which the foliation is due to the parallel arrangement of relatively large crystals of platy minerals. Muscovite, chlorite, and talc are the important platy constituents. Feldspars are rare, but quartz, garnet, and hornblende are common accessory minerals.

Hand specimen

Photomicrograph (X20)

Figure 103. Schist.

Mica crystals

54

Hand specimen

Figure 104. Schist.

Photomicrograph (X20)

Garnet   Mica

Hand specimen

Figure 105. Gneiss.

Photomicrograph (X20)

Mica   Quartz

Hand specimen

Figure 106. Gneiss.

Photomicrograph (X20)

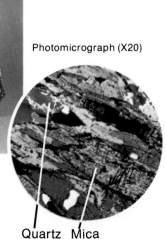

Quartz   Mica

Schists may be further classified on the basis of the more important minerals present. The most common types are chlorite schists, muscovite schists, hornblende-mica schists, and garnetiferous-mica schists. The unifying characteristic of all, regardless of composition, is that the *foliation* results from the parallel arrangement of platy minerals.

GNEISSES. Gneisses are metamorphic rocks in which the foliation results from *layers* of different mineral groups (Figures 105 and 106). Feldspar and quartz are the chief minerals, with minor amounts of mica, amphibole, and other ferromagnesian minerals. Gneisses thus resemble granite in composition, but are distinguished from them by the foliation. The foliation in a gneiss may range from semicontinuous layers of light and dark minerals (Figure 105) to highly contorted, well-defined layers such as are shown in Figure 106. In many deposits, layers expressing the foliation are several inches thick.

Gneisses are among the most abundant metamorphic rocks. They represent a high grade of metamorphism and may originate from various granite-rhyolite rocks or from lower-rank metamorphic and sedimentary rocks.

Foliated metamorphic rocks contain some of the most significant and striking evidence of the mobility of the earth's crust throughout time. They are believed to be formed in the roots of ancient mountain systems and are thus considered records of previous plate movements. They represent the end product of differentiation of the mantle into lighter continental crust, a process beginning with (1) partial melting of the mantle beneath a spreading center to form new oceanic crust; (2) partial melting of the oceanic crust at the subduction zone to form granitic and andesitic magmas (both (1) and (2) are types of magmatic differentiation); (3) sedimentary differentiation by weathering, erosion, transportation, and deposition of previous orogenic material into a geosyncline; and (4) deformation of the geosynclinal sediments into an orogenic belt with schist and gneissic rock formerly in the mountain roots.

Hand specimen

Figure 107. Metaconglomerate.

Photomicrograph (X20)

Quartzite matrix   Quartzite pebble

Hand specimen

Figure 108. Quartzite.

Photomicrograph (X20)

Deformed sand grains

Hand specimen

Figure 109. Marble.

Photomicrograph (X20)

Calcite crystals

Nonfoliated Rocks

METACONGLOMERATES. A metaconglomerate is a conglomerate which has been altered under heat and pressure to the extent that the individual pebbles are stretched, deformed, and fused together (Figure 107). Commonly, the stretched pebbles will show a definite lineation which is related to the orientation of stresses, but the rock is not foliated. Most metaconglomerates are so indurated that they fracture across the pebbles as easily as around them. Under the microscope, the sand-silt matrix of the conglomerate will show deformation similar to that exhibited in the pebbles.

QUARTZITE. Quartzites are nonfoliated metamorphic rocks composed principally of quartz. In some deposits quartz is the only mineral present. The individual grains in quartzites are deformed, interlocked, and fused together, so the rock breaks across the grains indiscriminately (Figure 108). Pure quartzite is derived from quartz sandstone, but some quartzites may contain as much as 40 percent other minerals, mica being one of the most abundant. Although quartzites are nonfoliated, some formations contain incipient slaty cleavage or relic bedding which imparts a planar element to the rock.

MARBLE. Marble is a nonfoliated metamorphic rock composed principally of calcite or dolomite. The crystals are commonly large and interlock to form a dense crystalline rock (Figure 109). Bands or streaks or organic impurities resulting from flowage or extreme deformation are common in some deposits. Colors may be white, pink, blue gray, or brown. Like limestone, a marble is characterized by its softness and its effervescence with hydrochloric acid.

The Origin of Metamorphic Rocks

The great bulk of metamorphic rocks are believed to have formed in orogenic belts at converging plate margins, and they represent an important phase in the growth of continents (Figure 110). The major steps in this process may be summarized as follows:

Sediment derived from erosion of the continent (or island arc) associated with the subduction zone is transported to the continental margin and deposited. This thick accumulation of sediment has been referred to as a geosyncline. As convecting currents in the mantle shift, the direction of plate movement changes, and ultimately the continent collides with another plate and the geosyncline is deformed into a mountain range. The tremendous horizontal pressures from the colliding plates cause the rocks in the roots of the mountain belt to partly melt and recrystallize. New minerals grow under the horizontally directed stresses and typically develop a foliation which is perpendicular to the stress, or essentially vertical. Some completely melted rock material rises toward the surface and may cool as dikes injected between the planes of foliation. Erosion of the mountains causes the orogenic belt to rise from isostatic adjustment, and ultimately the metamorphic rock formed deep in the mountain root is exposed at the surface and forms a new segment of the continental shield. Repetition of this process causes the continent to grow as geosynclinal sediments are welded to the shield with each orogenic event.

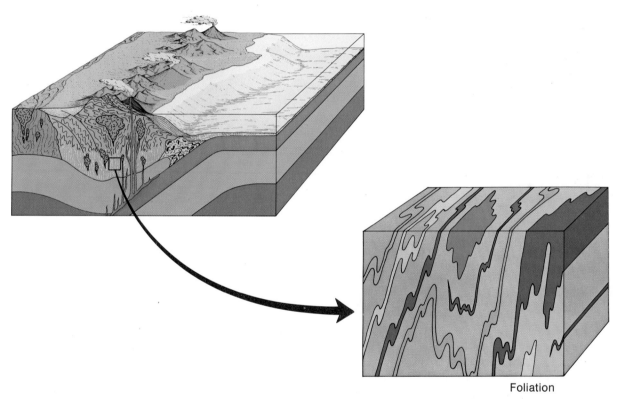

Foliation

Figure 110. The origin of metamorphic rocks.

Problems

1. Identify the rock specimens provided by your instructor. Proceed as follows:
   a. Determine whether the rock is foliated or nonfoliated.
   b. If the rock is foliated, determine the type of foliation.
   c. Determine the mineral composition.
   d. With this information refer to Table 6 and determine the rock name.
   e. On the basis of texture and composition determine the original rock type.

6 Lunar Rocks

The samples of lunar rocks brought back from the Apollo missions provide an important insight concerning the composition and history of the moon. The major rock types may be classified as follows:

1. Basalt—igneous rock from the maria.
2. Gabbro (anorthosite)—derived from the terrae.
3. Breccia—formed by fragmentation of surface material by meteorite impact.
4. Glass—formed by shock melting and rapid cooling during meteorite impact.

Figure 111. Basalt from the maria.

Although the lunar rocks contain some unusual textures and minerals, they are not strange or unique but closely resemble rocks on earth formed by similar processes.

Problems

1. Compare the thin section in Figure 111 with those shown for igneous rocks (pp. 27-31). Why is this rock classified as a basalt? What does this rock type indicate concerning geologic processes on the moon?

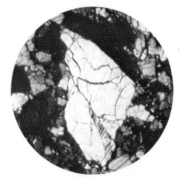

Figure 112. Gabbro (anorthosite) crushed by impact.

2. The rock shown in Figure 112 is composed almost entirely of plagioclase. What evidence indicates that the minerals were once in a liquid state? Why would you classify this rock as a gabbro?

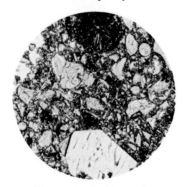

Figure 113. Breccia.

3. What textural features are distinctive of breccia (Figure 113)? How is breccia produced on the moon? Why is it a dominant rock type on the lunar surface?

7 Aerial Photographs and Topographic Maps

The study of geologic processes and their effect upon the earth's surface is a significant part of physical geology. Running water, ice, wind, ground water, vulcanism, and earth movements have continually acted upon the earth throughout geologic time and have produced an infinite variety of surface features. From a careful study of local and regional landforms it is possible to determine what processes are actively modifying an area at present and what processes were important in the past. The basic tools for such a study are topographic maps and aerial photographs. These are scale models of a portion of the earth's surface, showing details of the size, shape, and spatial relationships of landforms. In a sense, they give to physical geology what the microscope gives to biology—a new perspective.

This excercise explains how to view aerial photographs and read topographic maps and indicates how they can be used to study and interpret geologic processes and the landforms created by those processes.

Aerial Photographs

Aerial photographs are extremely useful in the study and interpretation of geologic problems because they provide an accurate model of the earth's surface. Moreover, most vertical aerial photos are taken in stereo, so that by using a simple lens stereoscope you can see the image in three-dimensional relief. Aerial photographs permit remarkably detailed study of many natural features of the earth's surface, such as vegetation types, intricacies of drainage patterns, rock outcrops, and the tone and texture of the land surface. Topographic maps, on the other hand, express only the morphology of the earth's surface, by means of contour lines. The most serious limitation of aerial photographs is distortion of both scale and location, because a photo is a conical projection and there are no quantitative data on elevations.

The primary purpose of using aerial photos in this manual is to illustrate geologic processes and the resulting landforms and to give you an opportunity to analyze and describe various geologic phenomena.

Stereoscopic Viewing

Aerial photos are usually taken in sequence along a flight line so that there is about 60 percent overlap in the flight direction and 30 percent overlap of flight strips. Every point on the surface photographed is shown on at least two different photos. When two adjacent photos along the flight line are viewed through a stereoscope in such a way that each eye sees only one of the two photos, the brain combines the images to produce the effect of a three-dimensional view of the surface. Thus, hills and valleys appear to stand out in bold relief. Many of the vertical aerial photographs in this manual are printed so as to permit stereoscopic viewing with a standard lens-type stereoscope. By following the steps outlined on page 197, you can become proficient in stereo viewing.

Interpreting Aerial Photographs

Interpreting aerial photos is a skill acquired only by considerable experience, but you can understand many aspects of photo interpretation if you understand some basic characteristics of land features as they appear on aerial photos. Some common geologic features seen on aerial photos are illustrated in Figure 114. Their appearance can be summarized as follows:

1. *Water*—Tones are dark gray or black except where sunlight is directly reflected. Likewise, water in soil and rock renders a darker tone.
2. *Vegetation*—Produces many different patterns. Forests are dark gray, grasslands are lighter tones, and cultivated fields are usually rectangular.
3. *Bedrock*—Different rock types are expressed by characteristic tones, textures, drainage patterns, features, and the selective growth of vegetation.

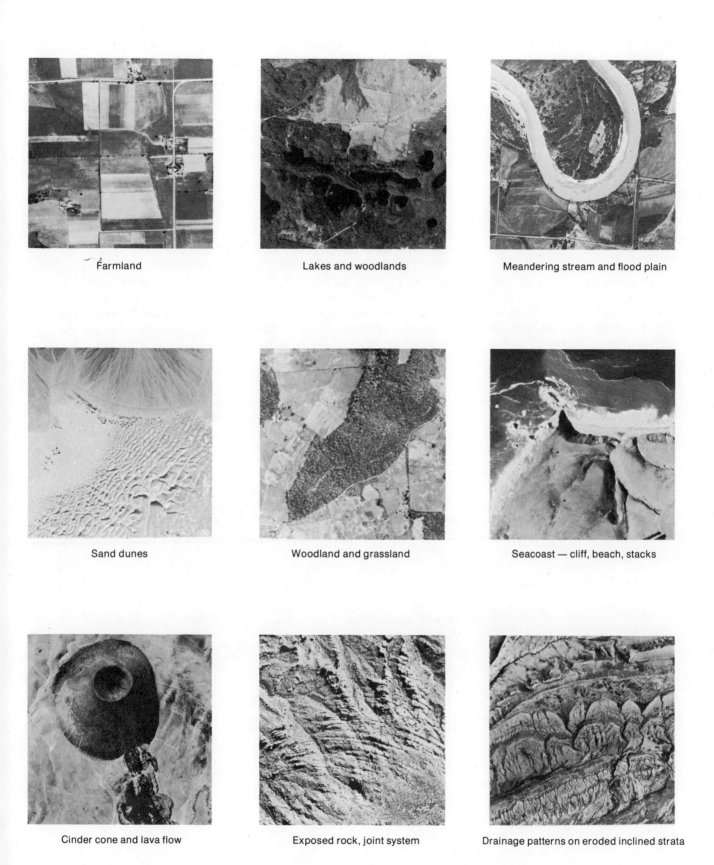

Farmland

Lakes and woodlands

Meandering stream and flood plain

Sand dunes

Woodland and grassland

Seacoast — cliff, beach, stacks

Cinder cone and lava flow

Exposed rock, joint system

Drainage patterns on eroded inclined strata

Figure 114. Examples of features visible on aerial photographs.

Contour Lines

Topographic maps are indispensable aids to many geologic studies. They show the configuration of the earth's surface by contour lines and permit one to measure horizontal distances and vertical elevations. A contour line is a line connecting points of equal elevation. Natural expressions of contour lines are illustrated by elevated shorelines, cultivated terraces, and patterns developed from contour plowing.

The idea of contours may become clearer to you if you think of an island in a lake and the patterns made on it when the water level recedes. The shoreline represents the same elevation all around the island and is thus a contour line (Figure 115). Suppose that the water level of the lake drops 2 feet and that the position of the former shoreline is marked by a gravel beach. Now there are two contour lines, the lake level and the old stranded beach, each accurately depicting the shape of the island at these two elevations. If the water level should continue to drop in increments of 2 feet, additional contours would be formed. A map of the beach is in essence a contour map (Figure 115D) and graphically represents the shape of the island and its elevation.

The relationship between a contour map and the features it expresses is illustrated in Figure 116. The conical hills are represented by a series of roughly circular contour lines. As the elevation increases to the crest of the hills, the circles become smaller. A careful study of this diagram reveals the following characteristics of contour lines:

1. Contour lines do not cross or divide.
2. Closely spaced contour lines represent steep slopes; contours spaced far apart represent gentle slopes.
3. Contour lines trend up valleys, cross streams, and return down the valleys on the opposite side, thus forming a V that points upstream.

On standard topographic maps, index contours (generally every fifth contour line) are labeled with their elevation and printed darker for easy identification. Lighter contours are not labeled, but their elevations can easily be determined. Count up or down from the nearest index contour and multiply by the contour interval. The contour interval is indicated at the base of the map. The most frequent interval used on 7½-minute and 15-minute quadrangles is 20 feet, although 5, 10, 40, 50, 100, and 200 feet are used if needed to express the topography being mapped.

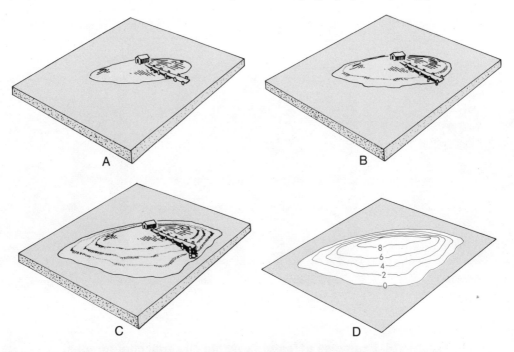

Figure 115. Diagram illustrating the concept of contour lines.

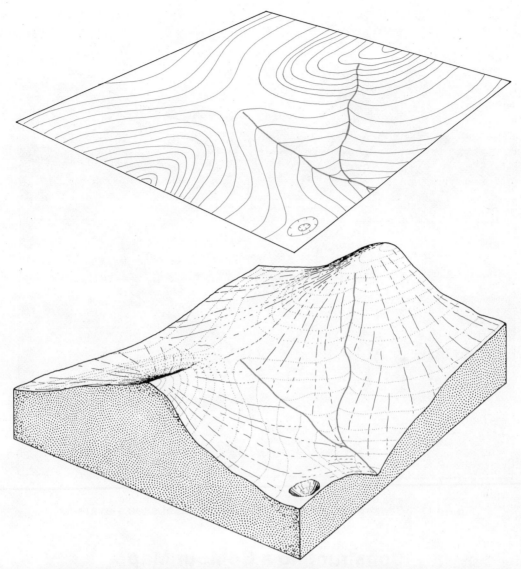

Figure 116. Diagram of the relationship between topographic features and contour lines.

Determining Elevations

Elevation refers to height (in feet or meters) above sea level and is essentially synonymous with altitude. Specific elevations are shown on topographic maps in various ways and are usually located at centers of towns, on hilltops, and at the bottoms of depressions. Elevations between contour lines can be approximated by interpolation. For example, a point midway between the contours 1240 feet and 1260 feet would most likely be 1250 feet, and a point located just below the 1260-foot contour line would probably be close to 1258 feet or 1259 feet. Such approximations are based on the assumption that the slopes have a constant gradient and the elevation is proportional to the horizontal distance. This, of course, is not always true, but a careful study of slope trends permits one to accurately estimate elevations between contours.

Relief is the difference in elevation between high and low points. You can easily determine the local relief of an area by subtracting the lowest elevation from the highest elevation.

Height and *depth* are measurements made relative to some local feature. For example, a monument might be 555 feet high relative to the ground and have an elevation (at its top) of 1555 feet because the ground it is on is 1000 feet above sea level.

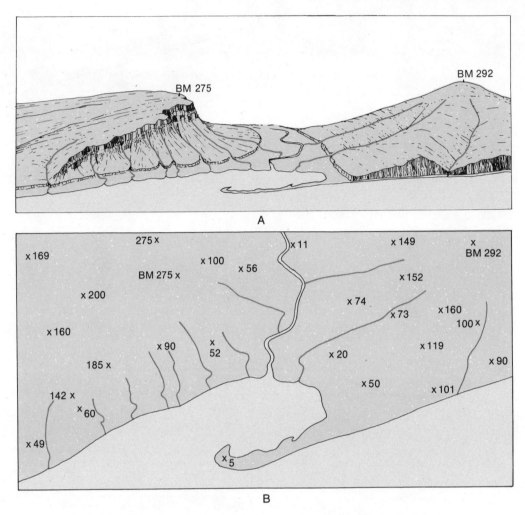

Figure 117. Constructing a contour map from established elevations.

Constructing a Contour Map

Contour lines on topographic maps are constructed from stereo aerial photographs by using high-precision plotting instruments which can read elevations, under ideal conditions, to the nearest foot. Prior to the use of aerial photographs, topographic maps were constructed by establishing points of elevation and sketching in contour lines in the field.

Problem

1. Construct a contour map of the landforms shown in Figure 117A by plotting the contours on the planimetric map (Figure 117B). First analyze the surface in detail. Study the variations in slopes, stream valleys, cliffs, hilltops, etc. It may be advantageous to sketch lightly a number of contour lines in perspective directly on the diagram (117A). In sketching contours on the map, it is generally best to start near the edge at the lowest elevations and work up the major streams. Pay particular attention to the established elevation points and be sure all contour lines are in harmony with them. To find the approximate position of a contour line between two control points, study the slope shown on the diagram and estimate its map position. Note that the landforms in Figure 117A include (1) rounded hills, (2) sea cliffs, (3) a flood plain, (4) a plateau, (5) a river valley, and (6) a coastal plain. These features should all be expressed on the contour map.

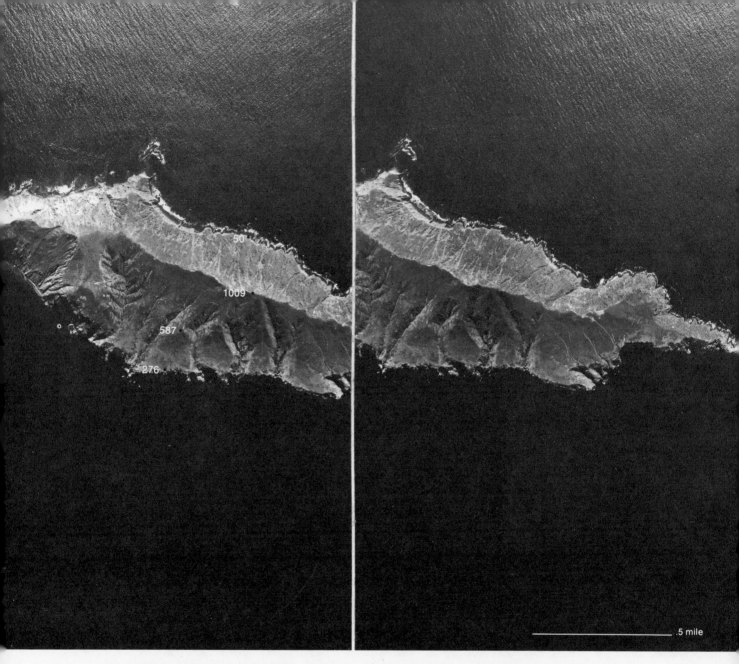

.5 mile

Figure 118. Constructing a contour map from stereo aerial photographs.

Constructing a Contour Map from Aerial Photographs

Aerial photographs provide the most accurate basis for constructing a contour map because one can see the surface in three dimensions directly from above.

Problems

1. Study the area shown in stereo in Figure 118. The water level provides a horizontal reference. Note the elevations established by a survey.

2. Trace contour lines across the entire area shown stereoscopically. Use a soft colored pencil because you may need to make a number of erasures before you are satisfied with your results. Use a contour interval of 200 feet. It is generally best to start with the lower elevations and work up major streams. Label every fifth contour.

3. How could you increase the amount of topographic detail?

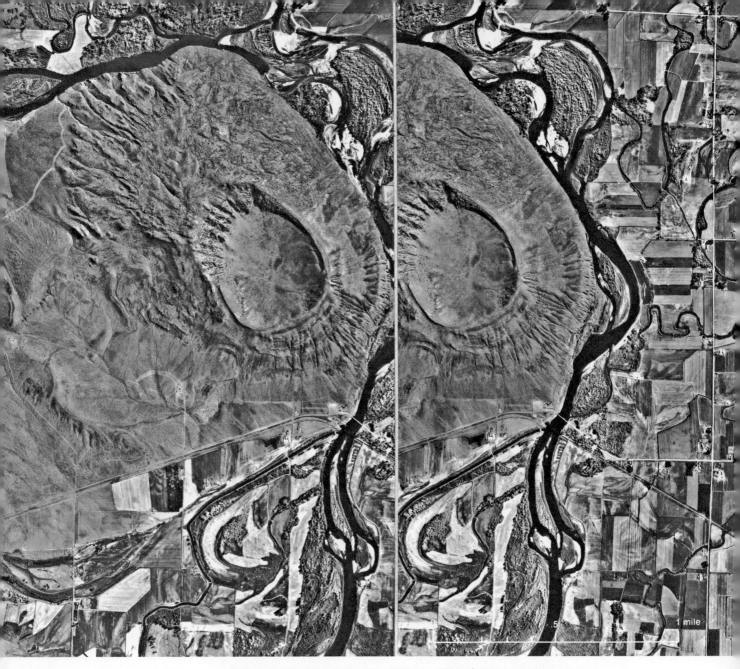

Figure 119. Aerial photo of Menan Buttes area, Idaho.

Comparison of Aerial Photographs and Topographic Maps

The Menan Buttes area offers an excellent opportunity to study the way simple topographic forms are expressed by contour lines. By carefully examining the photograph (Figure 119) with a stereoscope and comparing the image with the topographic map (Figure 120), you can soon develop the ability to visualize topographic forms in three dimensions just by looking at a contour map. The following problems will help you compare the map and the photograph.

Problems

1. Study the volcano of Menan Buttes. The slopes of the crater differ significantly from one side to the other. How are steep slopes expressed by contour lines?

2. How are the more gentle slopes at the base of the volcano expressed by contour lines?

Figure 120. Topographic map of Menan Buttes area, Idaho.

3. How are the rugged slopes in the northwest part of the crater expressed by contour lines?

4. How is the closed depression of the crater expressed by contour lines?

5. Study the flood plain area to the south of the butte. How is a relatively flat surface expressed by contour lines?

6. Sketch the form lines of the topographic surface that is in stereoscopic view and compare your results with those shown on the topographic map.

7. What are the advantages of an air photo? What are the advantages of a topographic map?

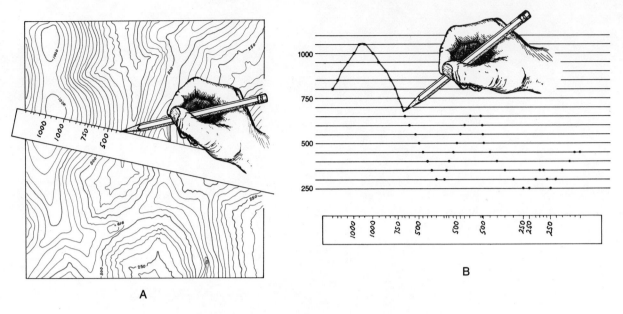

Figure 121. Constructing a topographic profile.

The Topographic Profile

Topographic maps present a view of the landscape as seen from directly above, an excellent perspective from which to examine regional relationships. This view, however, is unnatural, for we are accustomed to seeing hills and valleys from a horizontal perspective. In detailed studies of landforms it may be desirable to construct a profile, or cross section, through certain critical areas so that various features can be analyzed from a more natural viewpoint. A profile can be constructed quickly and accurately along any straight line on a map, according to the following procedure:

1. Lay a strip of paper along the line where the profile is to be constructed (Figure 121A).
2. Mark on the paper the exact place where each contour, stream, and hilltop crosses the profile line.
3. Label each mark with the elevation of the contour it represents. If contour lines are closely spaced, it is sufficient to label only the index contours.
4. Prepare a vertical scale on profile or graph paper by labeling horizontal lines to correspond to the elevation of each index contour line.
5. Place the paper with the labeled marks at the bottom of the profile paper and project each contour onto the horizontal line of the same elevation (Figure 121B).
6. Connect all the points with a smooth line.

Obviously, the appearance of the profile will vary depending on the spacing of the horizontal lines on the profile paper. If the vertical scale is the same as the horizontal scale, the profile, except on very small-scale maps or in areas of extremely rugged topography, will be nearly flat. Therefore, the vertical scale is usually exaggerated to show local relief.

To determine the gradient of a stream, measure a representative section of the stream and divide that distance (in miles) into the vertical difference (in feet) between the starting point and the end point. The result is the change in elevation expressed in feet per mile (ft/mi).

8 Regional Geomorphic Features of the United States

Objective

To review the relative size and spatial relationships of major physiographic features of the United States so you can better understand the significance of local landforms.

Main Concept

North America contains a number of physiographic provinces, which have distinctive landforms, rock bodies, and geologic structures.

Supporting Ideas

1. The major provinces of the United States can be recognized on a landform map.
2. River systems and coasts have many distinctive characteristics which reflect certain facts about their origin and history.

Discussion

The western third of the United States stands in marked contrast to the eastern two-thirds of the country. It is an area of geologically young mountains consisting of two main mountain chains: the Rocky Mountains in New Mexico, Colorado, Wyoming, Utah, and Montana; and the Coast Ranges of California, Oregon, and Washington. Between these two mountain chains is the Basin and Range Province (an area made up of discontinuous smaller ranges oriented north and south), the Columbia Plateau, and the Colorado Plateau.

In the eastern United States, the Appalachian Mountains extend from central Alabama to the mouth of the St. Lawrence River. This mountain chain is older than the western mountains and has undergone longer and more extensive erosion.

From the Appalachians to the Rocky Mountains, the central United States is a vast area of plains and lowlands developed on low-dipping to nearly horizontal rock units. This stable area has been only slightly disturbed by structural deformation. The Coastal Plains of the Gulf of Mexico and the Atlantic are the areas of lowland bordering the coast.

Problems

1. Draw the boundaries between the major provinces and make a summary list of the physiographic features that characterize each region.

2. Using different colored pencils, trace out on Figure 122 the drainage basins of (a) the Mississippi, Missouri, and Ohio rivers, (b) the Columbia River, (c) the Colorado River, and (d) the drainage system of the St. Lawrence River and the Great Lakes. Compare these four systems and briefly summarize their differences.

3. Compare the landforms of the New England, South Atlantic, Gulf, and Pacific coasts of the United States. Describe briefly the characteristic features of each.

Landform outline map of the
UNITED STATES
with adjacent parts of Canada and Mexico
by Erwin Raisz   WITHOUT LETTERING
Scale ⌐━━━━━━━━━━━━━━ ³⁰⁰ *Miles*
Copyright 1954 by Erwin Raisz

Figure 122. Landform Map of the United States by Erwin Raisz.

71

9 Evolution of Landscapes by Stream Erosion

Objective

To recognize different stages of landscape development that result from stream erosion and to understand the factors that influence their development.

Main Concept

Erosion of a landscape is not haphazard or random but proceeds in a systematic way so that landforms evolve through a series of stages in which the drainage network is extended upslope and the valleys are progressively deepened and widened. Ultimately, the landscape is reduced to a surface of low relief.

Supporting Ideas

1. The principal mechanics of erosion are (a) downcutting, which lowers the stream channel, (b) headward erosion, which extends the drainage system upslope, and (c) slope retreat, which causes the valley walls to recede laterally from the channel.
2. Each stage in the erosion of a landscape has a group of distinctive characteristics which are related to the proportion of the surface area in undissected divides, valley slopes, and valley floors.

Discussion

The basic process of stream erosion is the abrasive action of sand and gravel as they are moved by running water. By this process a stream deepens its channel, and, where other processes of stream erosion are minimal, abrasive action cuts steep, nearly vertical gorges. In addition to downcutting, every stream tends to erode headward and extend its channel upslope until it reaches the divide. As the drainage network grows larger by headward erosion and dissects the surface by downcutting, the valley walls become subject to a variety of slope processes, such as creep, debris flows, and landslides. These, plus the erosive activities of minor tributaries, cause the valley walls or slopes to recede from the river channel.

The diagrams in Figure 123 show how a newly uplifted area may evolve through a predictable series of stages until the landscape is eroded down to a surface of low relief near sea level. The rate at which the stages develop depends on climate, rock type, and other conditions. The terms early, middle, and late do not connote absolute periods of time, but simply refer to the degree to which the landscape is eroded.

Early Stage

1. Drainage is poor, with few streams per unit area; marshes and lakes may occupy shallow depressions.
2. Valleys are narrow and V-shaped and are separated by broad, nearly flat interstream divides. Most of the surface is undissected.
3. Downcutting and headward erosion are the dominant processes.

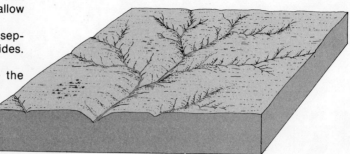

A

Middle Stage

1. A well-integrated drainage system is established with many streams per unit area.
2. Headward erosion has extended the drainage upslope to the divides.
3. Valleys are deeper and wider, with interstream divides narrow and rounded.
4. Local relief is at a maximum and most of the surface is the slopes of valleys.
5. Flood plains begin to develop.

B

Late Stage

1. Drainage is poor; streams have low gradients and meander over extensive flood plains.
2. Interstream divides are low and flat.
3. A few erosional remnants may exist as isolated hills (monadnocks), but the surrounding area is eroded to a peneplain. Most of the surface is eroded valley floor.

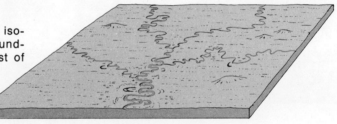

C

Rejuvenation

1. Uplift causes meanders to become entrenched and to develop deep canyons.
2. Erosion begins to dissect the peneplain surface.
3. Relatively steep gradients may be present which are out of harmony with the meander pattern.

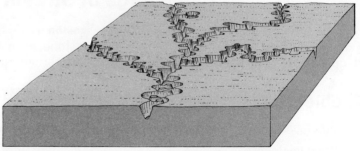

D

Figure 123. Block diagrams illustrating the stages of erosion of an uplifted area.

Figure 124. Mesa Verde, Colorado.

Early Stage of Stream Erosion

A region in the early stage of fluvial erosion is typified by the Mesa Verde Plateau of Colorado, an area eroded on horizontal sandstone formations. Steep-walled canyons contain major streams, and the areas between canyons are broad, flat, and undissected.

Problems

1. What geologic process is dominant in the stream channels?

2. What geologic process is dominant along the valley slopes?

3. Examine several tributaries to the main valleys. Is there any relationship between the size of a stream and the size of the valley through which it flows?

4. How will this area change as erosion continues?

74

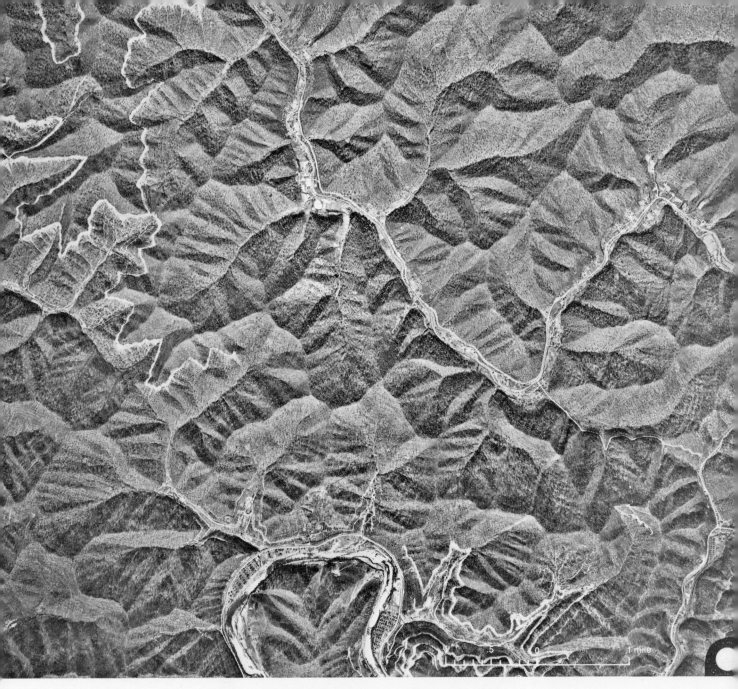

Figure 125. Allegheny Plateau, Pennsylvania.

Middle Stage of Stream Erosion

Western Pennsylvania typifies the middle stage of erosion in a humid climate. Horizontal sedimentary rock units composed of sandstone and shale underlie most of this region.

Problems

1. What is the major topographic difference between this area and that shown in the Mesa Verde photo?

2. Estimate the approximate percentage of area in valley floor, in valley slope, and in interstream divide. Is this an index of regional development?

3. In the northwest part of this area there has been extensive strip-mining for coal as indicated by the scars resembling a white contour line. What environmental problems may result from this activity?

Middle Stage of Stream Erosion

Figure 126 (p. 77). St. Paul, Arkansas

The topographic map of St. Paul, Arkansas, shows an area in a stage of erosional development intermediate between that of the previous examples of Mesa Verde and the Allegheny Plateau. Some topographic features of an early stage are still present, such as the plateau surface preserved on Brannon, Stacy, and Massey Mountains. A well-integrated drainage system has developed a relatively fine-textured topography replete with valleys and ravines. A maximum local relief is nearly established, the larger streams show a meandering pattern, and flood plains exist in the valleys.

Problems

1. Construct a profile along line A-A'. Label the landforms that indicate the middle stage and those that are remnants of an earlier stage. With a dashed line modify the St. Paul profile to show how it would have looked in the early stage of development. With a dotted line, indicate how it will look in the future.

2. Does the drainage pattern shown on the St. Paul map suggest a relationship between the size of streams and the size of the valleys through which they flow? What does this relationship suggest about the origin of valleys?

3. Estimate the relative percentage of area in valley floor, in valley slope, and in interstream divides on the topographic profile. Compare your findings with your answers to problem 2 for the Allegheny Plateau (p. 75).

4. Which process of stream erosion will terminate first in this area—downcutting, slope retreat, or headward erosion?

5. What process of mass movement will likely predominate in this area in the future—rock falls, creep, slumping, or debris flows?

6. If urbanization were to occur in an area such as this, what special geologic hazards should be anticipated?

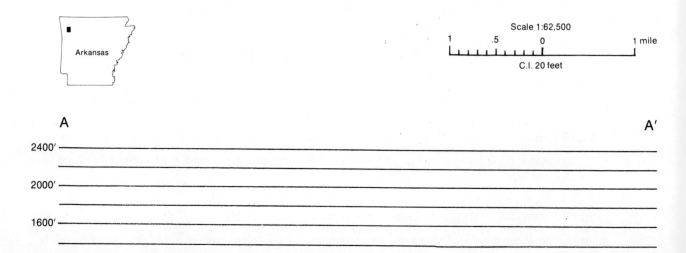

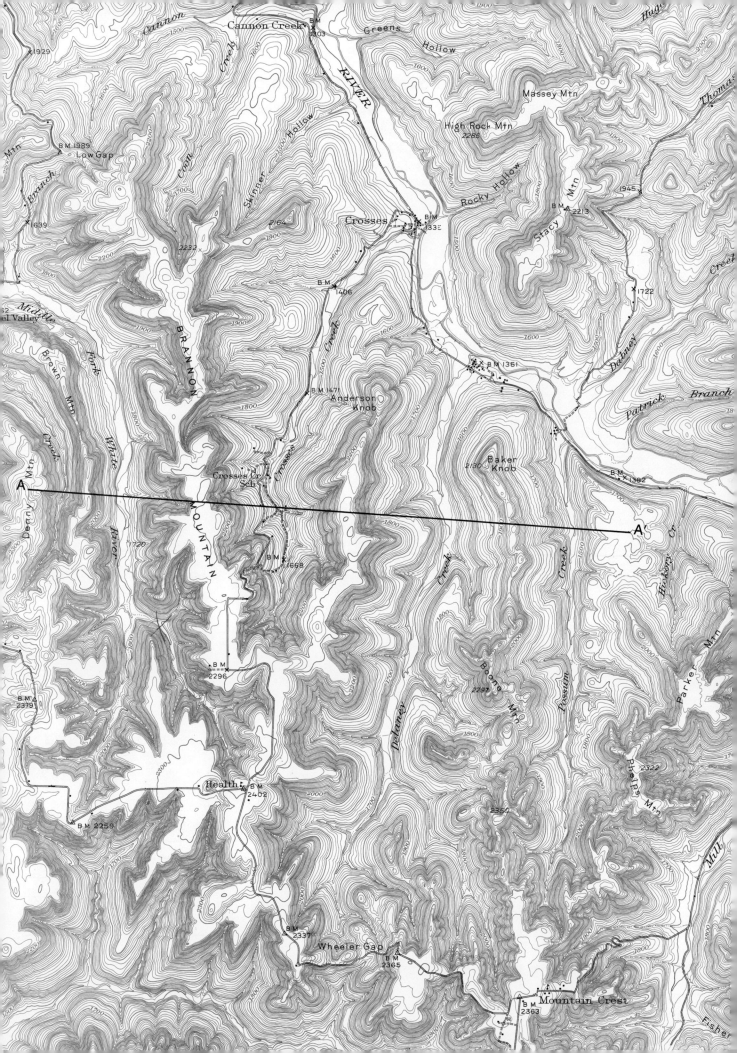

Late Stage of Stream Erosion

Figure 127 (p. 79). Stone Mountain, Georgia

Stone Mountain, the prominent knob in the central part of the map, is a small granitic intrusive body surrounded by gneisses and schists. The granite is more resistant to weathering and erosion than the gneisses and schists and has formed a conspicuous monadnock, whereas the surrounding area has been reduced to a broad, relatively flat surface between 960 and 1000 feet above sea level. This surface, in turn, appears to have been dissected by a second cycle of erosion.

Problems

1. Construct a topographic profile along line A-A'. Label the peneplain surface, erosional remnants of the first cycle, and areas being dissected by the second cycle of erosion.

2. List the criteria for a landscape in the late stage of stream erosion. Are the features shown on the Stone Mountain map and profile typical of a late-stage topography?

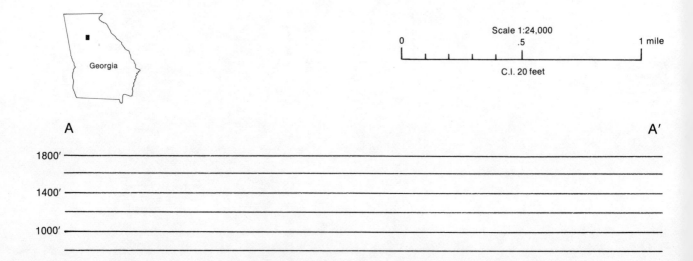

Georgia

Scale 1:24,000

0   .5   1 mile

C.I. 20 feet

A   A'

1800'

1400'

1000'

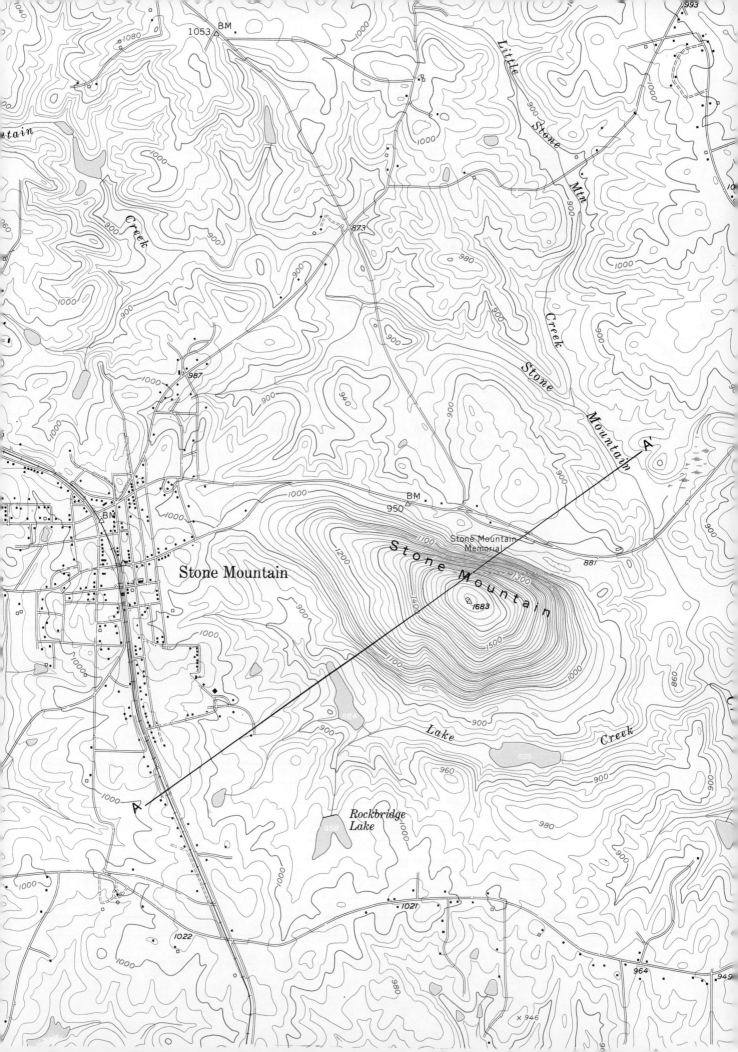

Rejuvenation

Figure 128 (p. 81). Anderson Mesa, Colorado

The meander pattern of the major river in the Anderson Mesa area of Colorado is typical of that produced in an old-age stage of the fluvial cycle, but instead of wandering across a flat flood plain, the meanders are entrenched in a steep-walled gorge. The explanation for this may be that the meanders have been inherited from an earlier old-age condition when the stream flowed on the surface of the plateau, which at that time was very near base level. Regional uplift caused the streams to cut downward into the plateau, and many of the characteristics of youth were rejuvenated. According to this explanation, then, the meandering stream pattern developed in the first cycle of erosion, was preserved, and became entrenched in a second cycle.

Problems

1. Draw a profile along line A-A', using the 100-foot interval contours. Label all landforms crossed by the profile. Use the profile and map in answering questions 2, 3, and 4.

2. What elevation probably represents the former level of the flood plain before the river was entrenched? What evidence can you cite to substantiate your answer?

3. Explain the striking difference between the stream in Spring Canyon and the major river. Is there any difference in the stages of development of these streams?

4. If the old-age erosional surface developed near sea level, what would be the minimum uplift which initiated the second cycle?

Colorado

Scale 1:24,000

0   .5   1 mile

C.I. 20 feet

A   A'

6000'

5500'

5000'

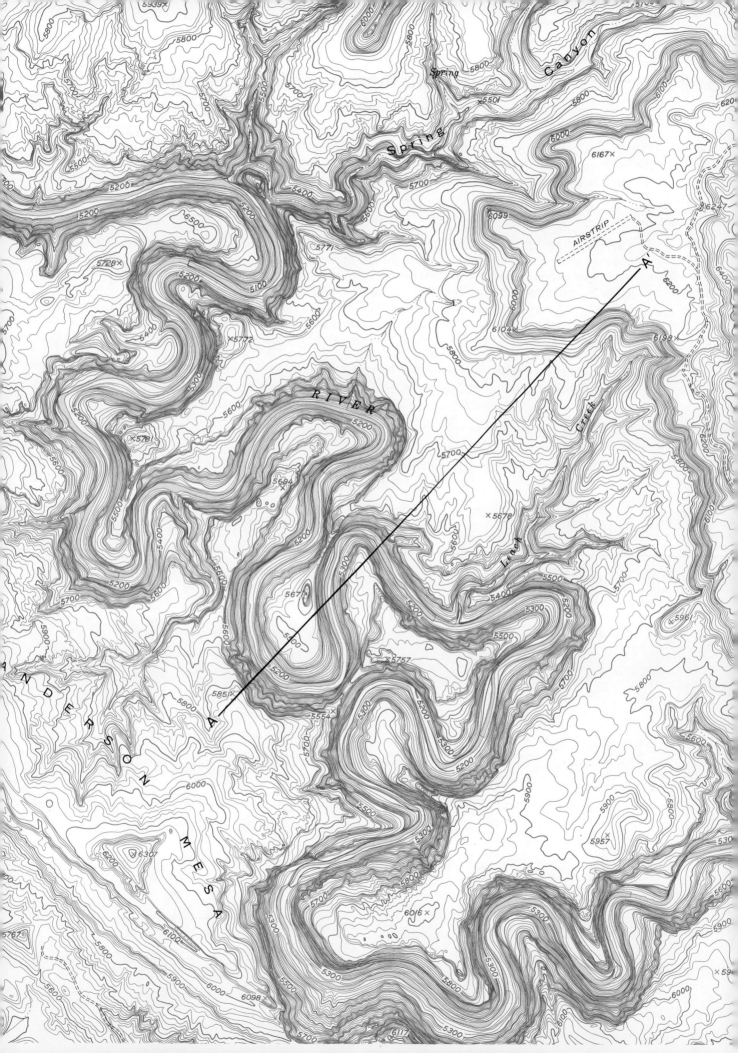

Rejuvenation and Superposition of Streams

Figure 129 (p. 83). Harrisburg, Pennsylvania

This map is an example of the small-scale topographic map series (1:250,000) published by the U.S. Geological Survey. All of the United States is covered by this scale of mapping, and although the maps lack local details, regional relationships are well illustrated. The area represented by this map is a classic segment of the Appalachian Mountains. A belt of strongly folded rocks forms the long, narrow ridges and intervening valleys. Each ridge is composed of a resistant bed of sandstone or conglomerate, whereas valleys are formed on weaker formations such as shale and limestone.

Crests of the main ridges have accordant elevations at approximately 1300 feet. This surface is interpreted to be the remnant of a peneplain produced when the region was near base level. The area has thus been rejuvenated at least once.

One of the most striking features of this area is the way the Susquehanna River has successfully cut across the resistant rock units. The sinuous course of the Susquehanna River is not controlled by rock structure but apparently was established on an older surface. When the region was uplifted the stream maintained its established course as it cut down into the underlying structure. The river is thus said to be superposed. Tributaries to the Susquehanna River, however, are strongly controlled by the structure of the underlying rocks and have developed by headward erosion along the strike of the less resistant beds, forming strike valleys.

Problems

1. Show by a heavy dashed line or in colored pencil the major tributaries to the Susquehanna River that developed by differential erosion along nonresistant strata. What type of drainage is this?

2. Show by a heavy solid line or in colored pencil those streams that were superposed. What was the original drainage pattern of the Susquehanna River and its tributaries? What features on the map influenced your answer?

Pennsylvania

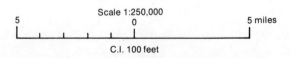

Scale 1:250,000

5   0   5 miles

C.I. 100 feet

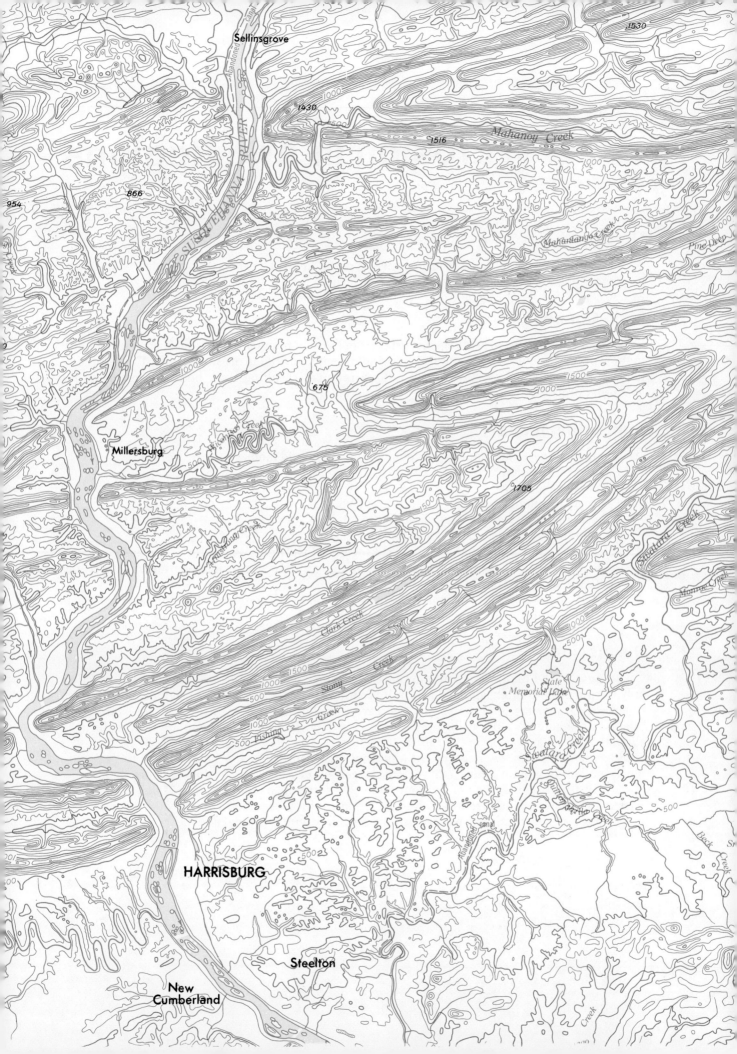

Sellinsgrove

Abandoned canal

1530

1430

1000

500

1516

Mahanoy Creek

954

866

Mahantango Creek

Pine Deep

SUSQUEHANNA RIVER

1500

675

1000

1705

Fishing Creek

Millersburg

500

Swatara Creek

Armstrong Creek

Monroe Creek

Clark Creek

1000

500

Creek

1500

1000

Stony

Creek

State
Memorial Lake

Swatara Creek

1000

500

Fishing

500

Creek

500

Swatara Creek

Manada canal

500

500

HARRISBURG

Beck Creek

Steelton

New
Cumberland

10 Erosion in Arid Regions

Objective

To recognize stages of landscape development in arid regions where block faulting is prominent and to understand the processes responsible for their development.

Main Concept

Erosional processes in arid regions differ from those in humid climates because of differences in the volume and intensity of water flow, in sediment load, and in erosional rates. Consequently, landforms in arid regions have many unique features resulting from both erosional and depositional processes.

Supporting Ideas

1. The factors most important in the development of an arid landscape are:
   a. low precipitation
   b. sparse vegetation
   c. poorly developed soil
   d. exceptionally large amounts of weathered debris
   e. infrequent, but sometimes heavy, local storms
2. The most characteristic feature of an arid region is insufficient water for drainage to continue to the sea. Thus, deposition of sediment carried by a stream occurs in topographic depressions such as fault-trough basins.
3. Faulted mountains and structural basins evolve through a series of predictable stages in which both erosion and deposition are important.

Discussion

Because of the limited precipitation in arid regions, most streams are intermittent and flow only during periods of exceptional rainfall. Weathering processes usually produce more decomposed rock fragments than the stream can carry, so that the streams are typically overloaded. When a stream enters a dry valley, the sediment is deposited near the mountain front to form an alluvial fan. This is especially true in the western United States, where block faulting has produced many closed depressions with internal drainage. The major landforms in this area are block-faulted mountain ranges in various stages of erosion and basins that are being progressively filled with sediment derived from the adjacent mountains. The block diagrams in Figure 130 show an idealized situation in which faulting occurred rapidly and the mountain ranges were subsequently worn down, filling the valley with erosional debris.

Early Stage

1. Maximum relief occurs in the initial stage owing to block faulting or folding. If recurrent movement along the faults does not take place, relief will diminish through time.
2. Alluvial fans build outward from the mountain front and basins become filled with erosional debris.
3. Shallow temporary lakes (playas) may form in the central part of the basin and expand or contract with fluctuations in climate.

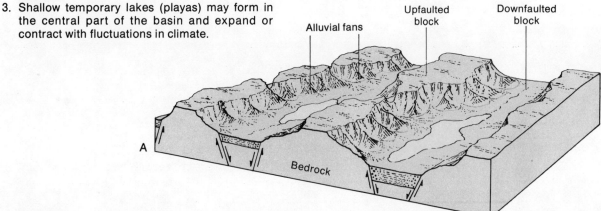

Middle Stage

1. The mountain mass is dissected into an intricate set of canyons, divides, and peaks. The mountain front has retreated from its original position.
2. Pediments develop along the mountain front.
3. Local relief diminishes.
4. Alluvial fans merge to form an alluvial slope called a bajada.

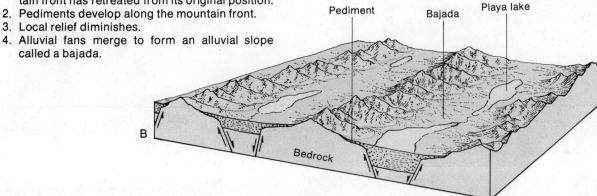

Late Stage

1. Intermontane basins are continually filled by erosional debris.
2. Pediments enlarge, and the mountain topography becomes smaller.
3. Ultimately only small, islandlike remnants (inselbergs) of the mountains remain, and most of the area is covered by debris.

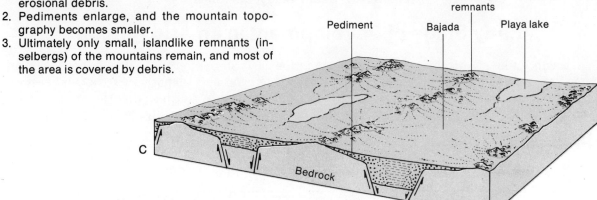

Figure 130. Block diagrams illustrating the stages of erosion in arid regions.

1   .5   0   1 mile

Figure 131. Death Valley, California.

Early Stage of Development in an Arid Region

Death Valley, California, is an arid region in the early stage of erosion. It is part of the Basin and Range Province, which extends from southern Oregon and Idaho across Nevada, eastern Utah, and Arizona into Mexico. The region is characterized by north-south-oriented mountain ranges and intervening fault-block basins. (See the physiographic map, Figure 122, pp. 70-71.)

Problems

1. Study the aerial photograph carefully. How many fans (large or small) can you see?

2. What factors (e.g., mountain height, climate, size of the drainage system) govern the size of an alluvial fan?

3. Draw a line showing the location of the fault along which the mountain was uplifted. Is there any evidence that recent movement has displaced some of the fans?

4. How would erosion and deposition in this area change if the climate became more humid?

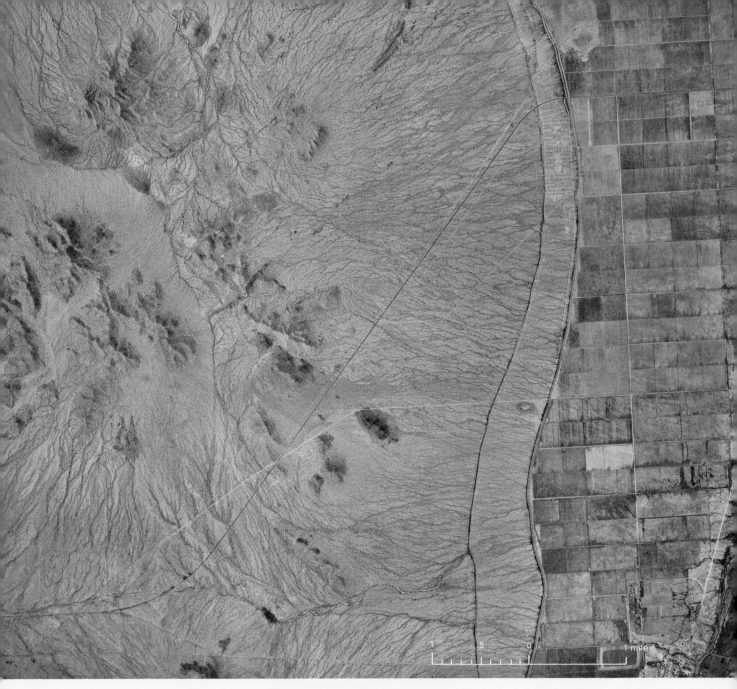

Figure 132. Sacaton, Arizona.

Late Stage of Development in an Arid Region

Sacaton, Arizona, part of the Basin and Range Province, is typical of an arid region in the late stage of topographic development.

Problems

1. On the Sacaton photo label the types of landforms that are shown.

2. How do the alluvial fans in this area differ from those in Death Valley, California?

3. Explain why Death Valley has a steep mountain front, but Sacaton has a highly irregular mountain front.

4. If the mountain range in this area was originally produced by faulting, where would the fault trace most likely occur?

5. Explain the origin of the closely spaced braided stream channels in this region.

6. How has the drainage in this area been modified by agricultural development?

Late Stage of Development in an Arid Region

Figure 133 (p. 89). Antelope Peak, Arizona

Antelope Peak, Arizona, is similar to Sacaton and Death Valley. The mountain masses are highly dissected, and many isolated remnants are partly buried by erosional debris.

Problems

1. Construct an east-west profile across the center part of the map, approximately one mile north of the main road. Distinguish between bedrock and unconsolidated alluvium, and label the landforms that are typical of arid regions.

2. What features indicate that this topography is in a late stage of development?

3. Note the absence of well-developed alluvial fans on the Antelope Peak map. How do you explain this?

4. How would the topography of this area be different if the climate were humid?

5. Water for irrigation in arid regions of the West must flow through canals across vast areas of alluvial slopes like the bajadas of the Antelope Peak area. What are some of the problems (geologic and climatic) of constructing canals and transporting water over this terrain?

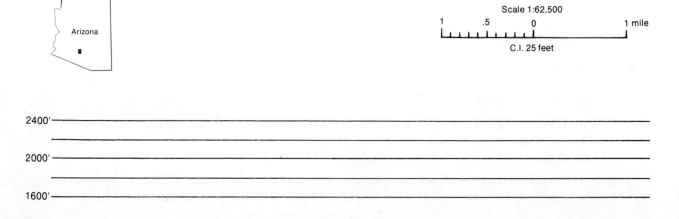

Arizona

Scale 1:62,500

1   .5   0   1 mile

C.I. 25 feet

2400'

2000'

1600'

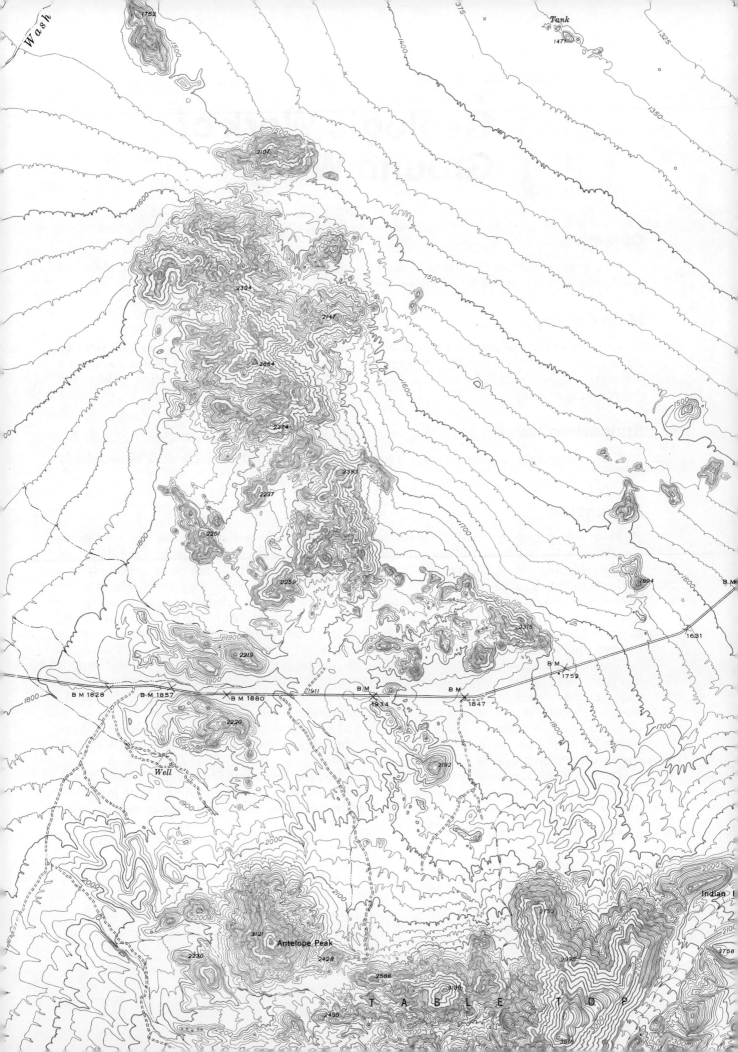

11 Geologic Work of Ground Water

Objective

To recognize the various stages in the development of karst topography and to understand how landscapes are formed by solution activity.

Main Concept

Solution activity of ground water is an important agent of erosion in regions underlain by soluble rocks, such as limestone, gypsum, and rock salt. Erosion by ground water develops a distinctive landscape called *karst* topography, characterized by sinkholes, solution valleys, and disappearing streams.

Supporting Ideas

Karst topography evolves through a series of stages until the soluble rock is completely removed.

Discussion

Karst topography typically develops in humid areas where horizontal or gently dipping limestone beds are exposed at the surface. Sinks and solution valleys constitute the dominant landforms, and much of the drainage is under ground. As a result, the region as a whole lacks a well-integrated drainage system. Tributaries are few and generally very short. Many minor streams suddenly appear as springs in blind valleys, flow for a short distance, and then disappear into sinkholes. Only major streams flow in a definite, open valley. Although solution activity and karst topography may predominate in certain localities, erosion by ground water is not a universal process as is erosion by running water.

An idealized sequence of stages in the evolution of karst topography is shown in the diagrams in Figure 134. In the early stage of development, solution activity develops a system of underground caverns that enlarge until eventually their roofs collapse, producing sinkholes. As the sinks increase in number and size, some of them merge to form solution valleys.

When solution valleys become numerous and interconnect, the area is considered to have reached the middle stage of development. A considerable part of the original surface is destroyed and maximum local relief is attained.

Continued solution activity ultimately erodes the area down to the base of the limestone unit and only scattered rounded hills and knolls remain. The area is then considered to be in the late stage of development because further erosion by solution activity can occur only if more limestone units exist in the subsurface.

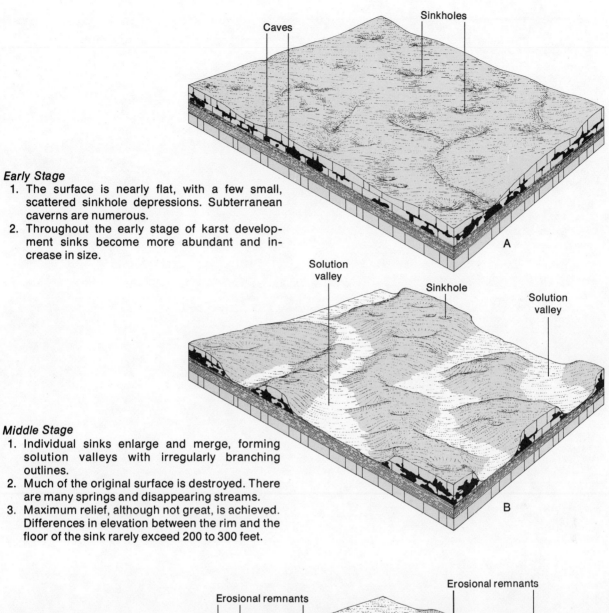

Early Stage

1. The surface is nearly flat, with a few small, scattered sinkhole depressions. Subterranean caverns are numerous.
2. Throughout the early stage of karst development sinks become more abundant and increase in size.

Middle Stage

1. Individual sinks enlarge and merge, forming solution valleys with irregularly branching outlines.
2. Much of the original surface is destroyed. There are many springs and disappearing streams.
3. Maximum relief, although not great, is achieved. Differences in elevation between the rim and the floor of the sink rarely exceed 200 to 300 feet.

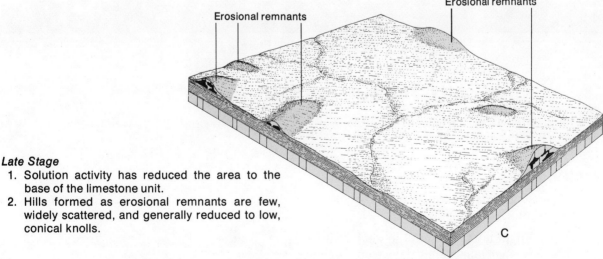

Late Stage

1. Solution activity has reduced the area to the base of the limestone unit.
2. Hills formed as erosional remnants are few, widely scattered, and generally reduced to low, conical knolls.

Figure 134. Block diagrams showing the evolution of karst topography.

Figure 135. Central Florida.

Early Stage of Karst Development

The bedrock in this area consists of horizontal layers of limestone. Local relief is only a few tens of feet.

Problems

1. With a colored pencil trace the drainage pattern shown in Figure 135. Is this pattern typical or atypical of karst topography?

2. Note the light tone surrounding some of the sinks. Considering the relationship of the water table to surface topography, how would you explain these tonal differences?

3. Explain why the series of sinks occurs in a straight line north of the road.

4. List the evidence indicating that this area is in the early stage of karst development.

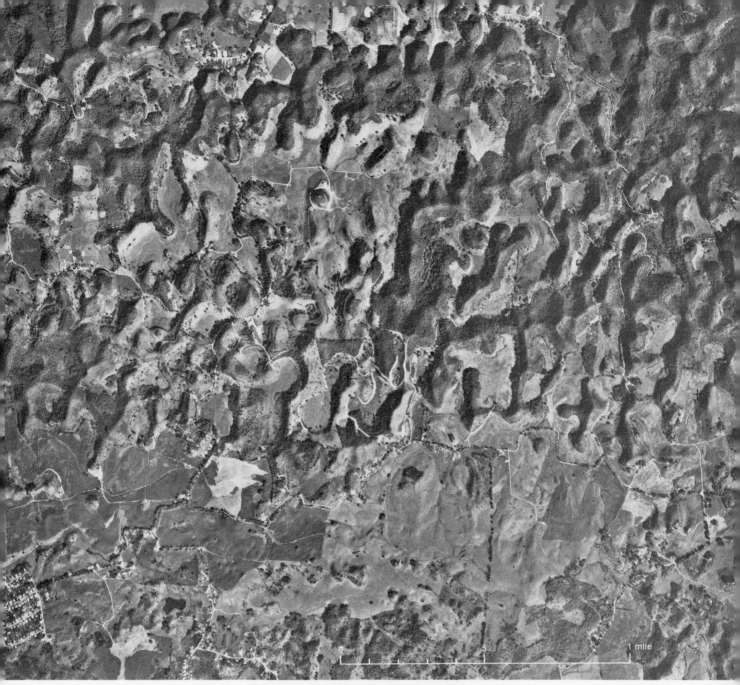

Figure 136. Manati, Puerto Rico.

Middle Stage of Karst Development

The bedrock in Manati, Puerto Rico, is nearly horizontal and consists of pure, dense limestone. Sinkholes in this region are as much as 150 feet deep and hills are up to 300 feet high.

Problems

1. Study the area shown in Figure 136 and compare it with the topography of the early and middle stages of stream erosion. List evidence indicating that this topography was not produced by stream erosion.

2. Explain the origin of the circular and elongate hills in this region. What features indicate the stage of erosional development?

3. Why are there only a few sinkholes in this area? Where do they occur?

Karst Topography

Figure 137 (p. 95). Mammoth Cave, Kentucky

The pockmarked surface of the Mammoth Cave area of Kentucky is a classic example of karst topography. Many of the sinks are aligned along joint systems, forming linear depressions. Some of the sinks south of Park City are more than 60 feet deep. North of Park City the number of sinks per unit area diminishes, but here there is a vast underground network of caverns. The northwest corner of the map is underlain by Mammoth Cave.

As you study this map, remember that closed depressions are indicated by circular or elliptical closed contours and hachures.

Problems

1. Study the map carefully and outline the large solution valleys.

2. Locate several disappearing streams and trace out the course of each. Do these streams show characteristics of a typical river system? What features of karst drainage patterns are unique?

3. Compare this area with the sequence of diagrams in Figure 134. Is it in the early, middle, or late stage of development? What specific features indicate the stage of development of this area?

4. What geologic hazards are most likely to be encountered in this area?

5. What particular problem of waste disposal and pollution does a karst area present to a city or industrial development?

6. Note the differences in topography in the northern, middle, and southern parts of the map, and consider the discussion on page 90. Does it appear that the stages in evolution of the landforms vary? How would you explain the differences in topographic development?

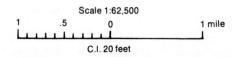

Scale 1:62,500

1   .5   0   1 mile

C.I. 20 feet

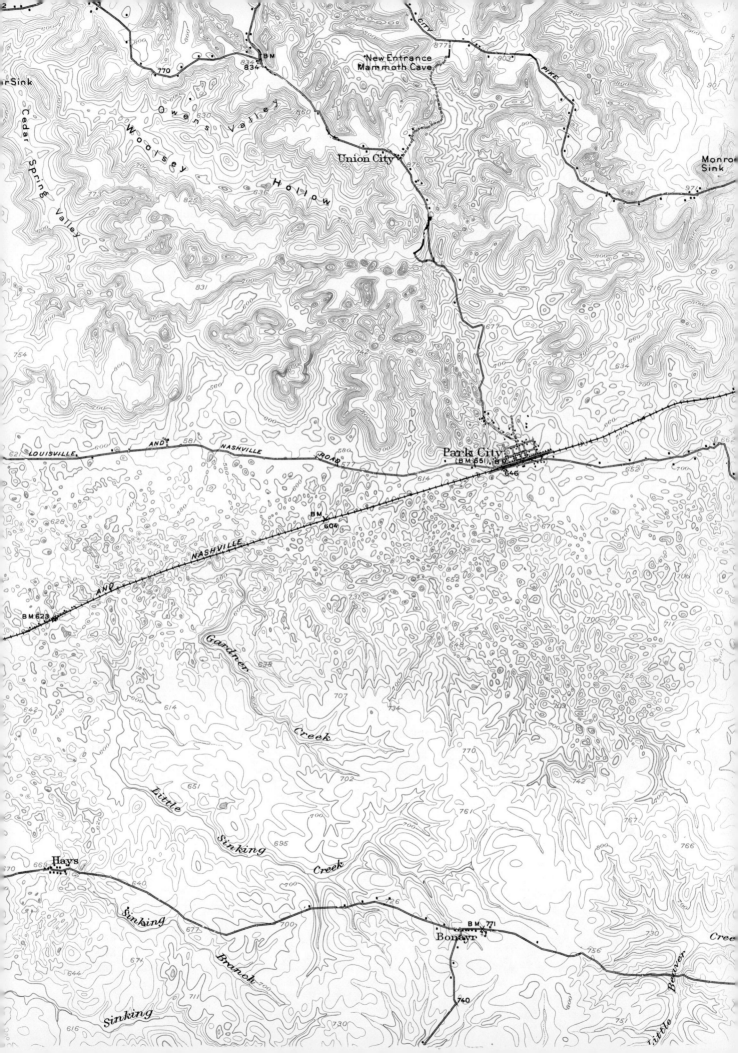

Karst Topography

Figure 139 (p. 97). Interlachen, Florida

The elevation of the lakes in this region provides much important information about the ground-water conditions. The surface of each lake is essentially the surface of the water table. Thus the lakes are control points for the elevation of the water table, and it is possible to construct a generalized contour map showing the configuration of the water table. For example, in Figure 138 the elevation of Dark Lake is between 120 and 130 feet, the elevation of Glass Lake is between 140 and 150 feet, and the elevation of Clear Lake is between 100 and 110 feet. For convenience, assume that the levels of these lakes are 125, 145, and 105 feet, respectively. The water table can be contoured by application of the same principles used in contouring the surface of land. The 140- and 130-foot contour lines would be located between Dark Lake and Glass Lake, and the 120- and 110-foot contour lines would be located between Clear Lake and Dark Lake. It is obvious that the water table slopes to the east.

Problems

1. Determine the elevation of most of the large lakes in this area and construct a contour map of the surface of the water table.

2. Many farms, small industries, and urban centers dump all their untreated liquid wastes into the subsurface. What happens to it?

3. What geologic hazards (floods, landslides, subsidence, earthquakes, erosion, etc.) are most significant in construction work in this area?

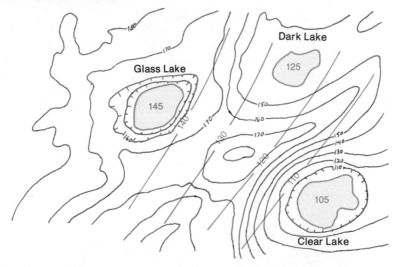

Figure 138. Diagram showing how to contour a water table.

Florida

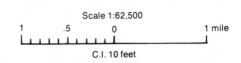

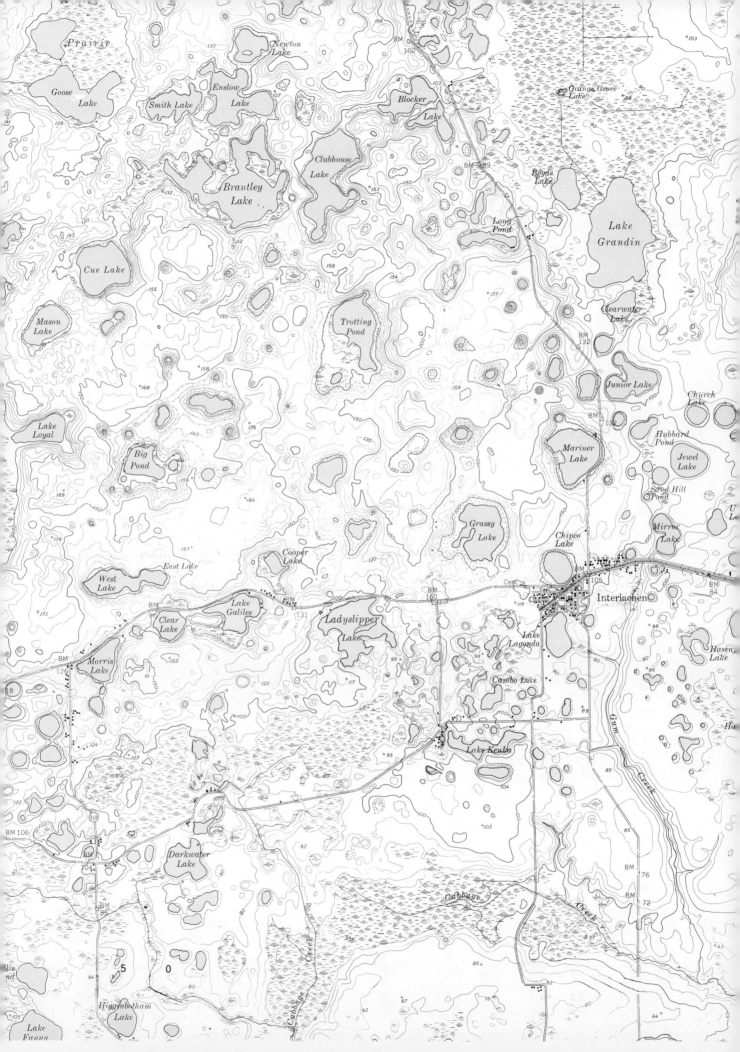

12 Volcanic Landforms

Objective

To recognize landforms resulting from volcanic activity and to understand how they evolve through a series of stages as a result of stream erosion.

Main Concept

Landforms developed by vulcanism are initially constructional features, which build up and add materials to the land surface. However, they are subject to stream erosion and evolve through a succession of stages from cinder cones and lava flows to isolated remnants of volcanic necks, dikes, and lava-capped buttes.

Supporting Ideas

1. Lava, being liquid, will flow down an existing slope and follow previously formed drainageways. The initial effect of lava flows on the topography is to clog, block, and displace the local stream system.
2. At first erosion is concentrated along the margins of the flows, where new drainage channels are established. As erosion proceeds along the flow margins, downcutting and slope retreat produce a lava-capped ridge called an inverted valley.
3. As erosion continues, the inverted valleys are dissected into isolated mesas and buttes, which may be over 1000 feet above the surrounding area.

Discussion

The diagrams in Figure 140 illustrate the evolution of landforms where local vulcanism has occurred. Figure 140A shows the early stage of development, in which lava flows are extruded, move downslope, and enter a drainage system. The lava flow follows the river channel and disrupts the drainage. Lakes may be impounded upstream from the flow, and the drainage is usually displaced so that streams are forced to flow along the margins of the lava. As a result, subsequent stream erosion is concentrated along the margins of the flow.

With continued erosion (Figure 140B), new stream valleys are cut along the lines of the displaced drainage and grow deeper and wider. The solidified lava occupying the former stream valley is usually far more resistant than the surrounding rock and is eroded into a long, sinuous ridge called an inverted valley. Cinder cones formed during the initial stage are rapidly eroded, leaving only the resistant lava in the conduit of the volcano, which protrudes above the surrounding surface as a volcanic neck.

Figure 140C illustrates the late stage of development. Erosion has lowered the landscape adjacent to the inverted valley so that lava-capped mesas and buttes stand as remnants high above the surrounding surface. Slope retreat along the margins of the inverted valleys reduces the lava flows to small buttes, which in time are completely eroded away. Volcanic necks and dikes then remain as the only evidence of volcanic activity.

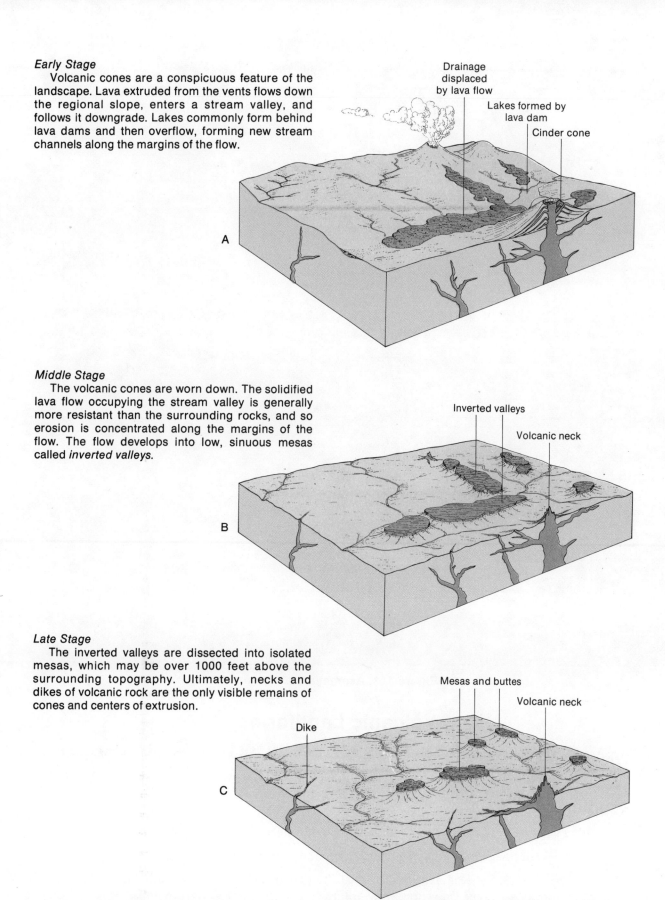

Early Stage

Volcanic cones are a conspicuous feature of the landscape. Lava extruded from the vents flows down the regional slope, enters a stream valley, and follows it downgrade. Lakes commonly form behind lava dams and then overflow, forming new stream channels along the margins of the flow.

Drainage displaced by lava flow

Lakes formed by lava dam

Cinder cone

A

Middle Stage

The volcanic cones are worn down. The solidified lava flow occupying the stream valley is generally more resistant than the surrounding rocks, and so erosion is concentrated along the margins of the flow. The flow develops into low, sinuous mesas called *inverted valleys*.

Inverted valleys

Volcanic neck

B

Late Stage

The inverted valleys are dissected into isolated mesas, which may be over 1000 feet above the surrounding topography. Ultimately, necks and dikes of volcanic rock are the only visible remains of cones and centers of extrusion.

Dike

Mesas and buttes

Volcanic neck

C

Figure 140. Diagrams illustrating the evolution of topography associated with volcanic activity.

Figure 141. Asamayama, Japan.

Volcanic Landforms

Asamayama is one of Japan's most active volcanoes. All of the material shown in this photograph is of volcanic origin.

Problems

1. Study Figure 141 and trace with a red pencil the outline of the major flow units.

2. Why is new drainage located along the margins of the flow?

3. The most recent flow was extruded in 1783. It is composed of andesite and shows a typical rough, blocky surface. Does the flow follow any topographic depressions? Has it been modified by erosion since it was extruded?

4. How many volcanic cones and cone remnants can you recognize in this area?

Figure 142. St. George, Utah.

Inverted Valleys

In the vicinity of St. George, Utah, several stages of vulcanism are represented by remnants of flows, some of which have evolved into inverted valleys and isolated buttes. The oldest flows are labeled I, younger flows II, and the most recent extrusions III.

Problems

1. Map the areal extent of flows I, II, and III, using a different colored pencil for each flow.

2. Note the small creeks on either side of flow III. How will erosion modify this flow with time?

3. Compare and contrast the surface features of flows II and III.

Ancient Volcanic Activity

Figure 143 (p.103). Ship Rock, New Mexico

The unconsolidated ash and cinders that make up many volcanic cones are easily eroded, and therefore the cone is readily obliterated. But lava, which congeals within the conduit, is generally very resistant and may remain as evidence of volcanic activity long after the cone is gone. The volcanic neck, or plug, gives some indication of the size of the original cone. Radiating dikes are commonly associated with volcanoes, and, like the neck, they are more resistant and may stand up as long, vertical walls.

Problems

1. Carefully study the topographic map of Ship Rock. Many volcanic features are very well defined but others are more subtle. On the topographic map sketch the volcanic features.

2. Measure the diameter and height of the volcanic neck and dikes. What is the thickness and length of the longest dike? What would be the minimum diameter of the cone?

New Mexico

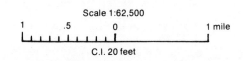

Scale 1:62,500

1   .5   0   1 mile

C.I. 20 feet

13 Shorelines

Objective

To recognize the major types of coasts and to understand the factors that control their development.

Main Concept

Most coasts can be classified on the basis of the geologic processes that have been most significant in determining their configuration. Two main types of coasts are distinguished: (1) coasts shaped mostly by terrestrial processes, such as running water, glaciation, and vulcanism and (2) coasts shaped largely by marine processes, such as marine erosion, marine deposition, and the growth of marine organisms.

Supporting Ideas

1. The worldwide rise in sea level associated with the melting of the glaciers has drowned many landscapes. The configuration of the present coasts may thus be due to a variety of geological processes that operated on the land before the sea level rose, not to marine processes operating now.
2. Coasts formed by subaerial erosion are notably irregular, with many bays and headlands.
3. Coasts formed by fluvial deposition contain many geographic features, such as stream channels, marshes, bays, spits, bars, and tidal flats.
4. Coasts formed by marine erosion are relatively irregular and usually contain some marine terraces, cliffed headlands, and small local sand beaches.
5. Coasts formed by marine deposition are characterized by beaches, bars, and spits and are remarkably straight.

Discussion

Most shorelines throughout the world have been greatly affected by the rise in sea level associated with the melting of the glaciers, and virtually all coasts have been submerged during the last 30,000 years. The result of submergence is that the river valley becomes embayed or drowned. This produces a highly irregular shoreline such as that of Chesapeake Bay.

Some coasts, however, show evidence of significant change since the sea approached its present level, because waves and currents have rapidly modified the preexisting topography.

The block diagrams in Figure 144 illustrate some of the major coastal types, based on the classification developed by F. P. Shepard.

Primary Coasts (Configuration due to terrestrial processes)

Stream Erosion

The configuration of the shoreline was developed by stream erosion when the area was not covered by the sea. A subsequent rise in sea level resulted from melting of the Pleistocene glaciers. River valleys were drowned.

Glacial Erosion

When glaciers melt and sea level rises, long arms of the sea extend many miles up the deep valleys. These drowned glacial valleys, called fiords, are not greatly modified by wave action.

Stream Deposition

Where major rivers enter the sea they commonly deposit more sediment than waves and currents can carry away, and new land is built up in the form of a delta. Deltaic coasts develop best in protected bays, where wave action is at a minimum.

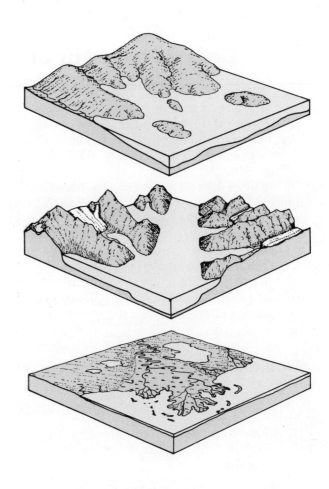

Secondary Coasts (Configuration due to marine processes)

Wave Erosion

In areas where the rock is relatively uniform, wave erosion forms straight sea cliffs. If a variety of rock types is present, wave erosion will produce bays in the soft material and leave the resistant rocks projecting into the sea as rocky points.

Marine Deposition

Coasts built by sediment deposited by waves and currents are readily recognized by their beaches, barrier islands, spits, and bars, with marshes and lagoons forming in protected areas.

Organically Built Coasts

The configuration of some shorelines is controlled by the growth of organisms such as coral reefs and mangrove trees.

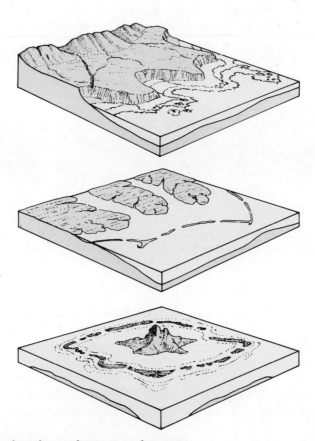

Figure 144. Diagrams illustrating the major types of coasts.

Coasts Formed by Subaerial Erosion—Fluvial

Figure 145 (p. 107). Washington, D.C.; Maryland; Virginia

The entire shoreline in the Chesapeake Bay area forms a very irregular dendritic pattern typical of a valley cut by stream erosion. These fluvial features have been preserved as the sea level has risen and drowned the region. To better visualize the regional setting of these drowned valleys, examine this entire area on the geologic map of the United States which your instructor will provide.

Estuaries like Chesapeake Bay commonly form shallow bodies of water that extend considerable distances inland. Typically, the original river valley is expressed by submarine contours that increase in depth seaward, just as rivers decrease in elevation downstream. In some instances, this profile is interrupted if an estuary is sealed off where longshore currents deposit a bar at its mouth.

In time, the fluvial aspects of an estuary will be lost as marine features form in response to erosion and deposition by wave and current action. A number of marine features have developed in Chesapeake Bay, and the originally irregular shoreline has been smoothed and straightened by the erosion of headlands and the deposition of spits and beaches. Additional changes in the bays occur as they become "silted in" and as marshes and tidal channels develop.

Problems

1. Construct a topographic profile along line A-A'. Include submarine and land contours. Label features that represent the original river valleys and features formed by marine processes.

2. Notice that parts of the shoreline have been modified by spits, cuspate beaches, and baymouth bars. Label these features on the map. What processes have controlled their formation?

3. The north side of the Potomac River estuary is irregular where numerous small tributary river valleys have been inundated. On the map, modify this shoreline to indicate how it will likely appear in the future as marine processes and sedimentation in the estuary continue.

Chesapeake Bay area

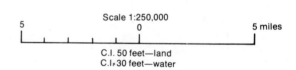

Scale 1:250,000

C.I. 50 feet—land
C.I. 30 feet—water

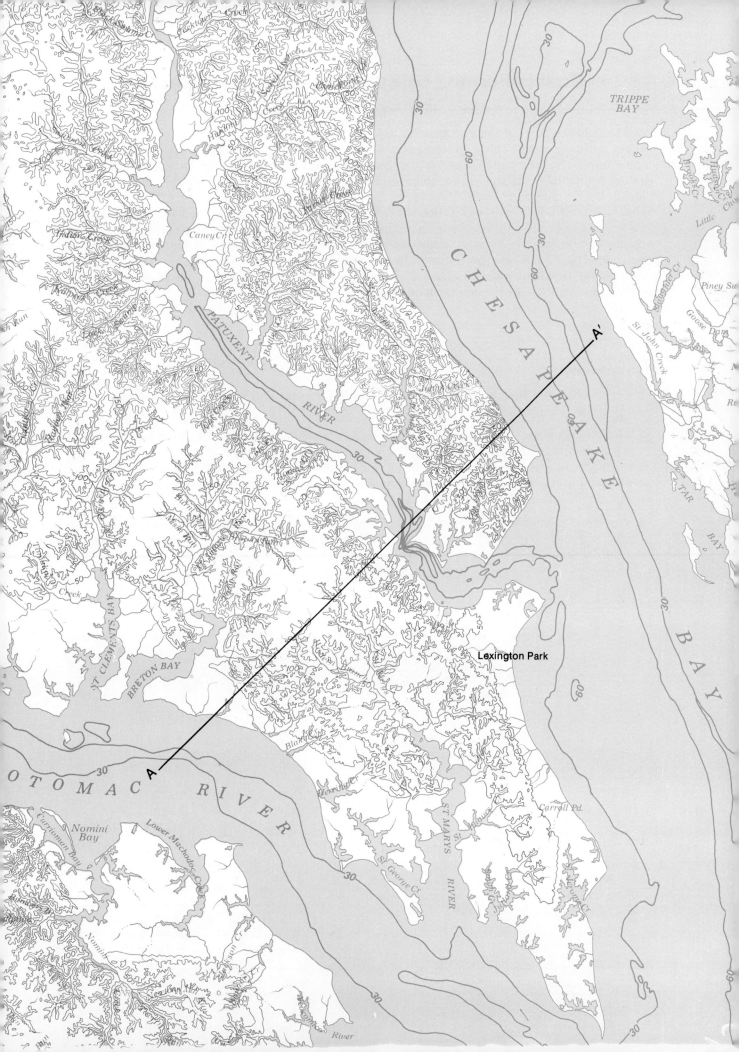

Coasts Formed by Subaerial Erosion—Glacial

Figure 146 (p. 109). Boothbay area, Maine

The Atlantic coast of the northeastern United States has had a complex history in relatively recent geologic time. The importance of glaciation in shaping the marine and terrestrial topography of New England is discussed in Exercise 15, Continental Glaciation. Factors important in developing the landscapes of much of the Boothbay area include the regional rock structures, glacial erosion and deposition, depression of the earth's crust from the weight of the ice sheet, subsequent rebound of the crust following removal of the ice, the effect of worldwide changes in sea level during and following glacial times, and, finally, the ever-present processes of wave erosion and deposition. Such a potpourri of events makes it extremely difficult to describe this coast. One can, however, use the modified version of Shepard's classification (Figure 144) to describe the Boothbay coast in terms of the most obvious process significant in developing its present topography—glacial erosion modified by submergence.

Problems

1. Study the land contours and submarine topography. What evidence is there of a recent rise in sea level?

2. On the basis of the area's topography (both submarine and surface), what has been the minimum rise in sea level?

3. Shoreline topographic maps commonly show numerous examples of marine erosion and deposition, regardless of the original sculpturing agent. Depositional features are usually most apparent as bays fill in and spits are built laterally from forelands. Features like this are common on the map of Chesapeake Bay (Figure 145). To what degree have marine erosion and deposition modified this topography?

4. Was the glaciation that occurred in this general area primarily erosional or depositional? Can you find sufficient information on this map to back up your answer? What field evidence would you seek to substantiate your answer?

Maine

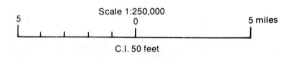

Scale 1:250,000

5   0   5 miles

C.I. 50 feet

Coasts Formed by Marine Deposition

Figure 147 (p. 111). Atlantic City area, New Jersey

Shorelines which build seaward by processes of marine sedimentation are referred to as marine depositional coasts. Most of the southeast and Gulf coasts of the United States are of this type. Within these regions, however, considerable variation can be observed. North and south of Chesapeake Bay there are long, sweeping spits and cuspate barrier islands, like those in the vicinity of Cape Hatteras. Further south, the Sea Island section of South Carolina and Georgia is made up of barrier islands and broad expanses of tidal marsh dissected by tidal inlets and rivers.

Problems

1. Explain the origin and evolution of the large barrier island or spit which runs north and south along the east side of the map.

2. Are the lagoons being filled with sediment now? What evidence can you cite for your answer?

3. Note that the lagoons in the southern part of the area are filled in more than those in the north. Explain why.

4. During the Pleistocene epoch, sea level was several hundred feet below the present level. How would this coastal area change if sea level fell approximately 50 feet?

5. How will the New Jersey coast change if sea level remains constant?

6. How will the coast change if sea level gradually rises?

7. What are the principal environmental hazards to be expected in this coastal zone?

8. Recreational development is common in areas such as this. What problems should be anticipated in this area as development proceeds?

New Jersey

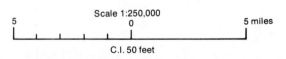

Scale 1:250,000

5   0   5 miles

C.I. 50 feet

Toms River

Long Beach

Egg Harbor City

Atlantic City

Ocean City

BARNEGAT BAY

Great Bay

ATLANTIC OCEAN

Coasts Formed by Subaerial Deposition

Figure 148 (p. 113). Mississippi Delta area

Coasts of subaerial deposition result from major rivers bringing sediments from the land and depositing them in the sea. Characteristic of this type of deposition are deltas that build seaward as rivers drop their sediment load upon reaching base level. Deltas can have various configurations, depending on the rate of sedimentation, the effect of tidal and longshore currents, and the depth of the sea.

The delta of the Mississippi River is probably the best known, and certainly the most thoroughly studied, delta in the world. It is an excellent example of subaerial deposition. It is building rapidly seaward as nearly 500 million tons of sediment are added to it annually. The river builds a birdfoot subdelta for a considerable distance and then is forced to shift its course, leaving the formerly active delta to be modified by waves and currents.

Problems

1. Study the configuration of the shoreline. How would you describe a coast controlled by stream deposition?

2. How many subdeltas can you recognize where the Mississippi once flowed?

3. How is the shoreline of a subdelta modified by marine processes after it has been abandoned and is no longer the site of active sedimentation?

4. How does this coast differ from coasts formed by (a) stream erosion, (b) marine erosion, and (c) marine deposition?

Louisiana

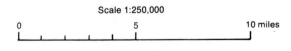

Scale 1:250,000

0   5   10 miles

Coasts Formed by Marine Erosion

Figure 150 (p. 115). San Pedro, California

A coastline developed by wave erosion is characterized by a steep cliff rising above a wave-cut terrace that slopes seaward at a low angle (Figure 149). Much of the western coast of the United States is of this type, with a narrow beach backed by a relatively straight line of cliffs rising to heights that in places exceed 500 feet. The eroding energy of the waves is concentrated at the base of the cliffs, and often a sea cave or a notch is formed. Slumping and landslide result from the undercutting and cause the cliffs to recede.

Problems

1. Construct a topographic profile along line A-A'. Label the depositional and erosional features on the profile and compare it with Figure 149.

2. As erosion of the land continues, the wave-cut terrace will become wider. What effect will a broad, shallow terrace have on the ability of waves to undercut the sea cliff?

3. Examine the gently sloping land surface between 100 feet and 300 feet on the San Pedro map and the topographic profile. What geologic agent could be responsible for the development of this surface?

4. How will this shoreline appear in the future? Will it most likely become straighter or more irregular?

5. What environmental hazards are to be anticipated in this coastal area? What type of construction restrictions should be considered?

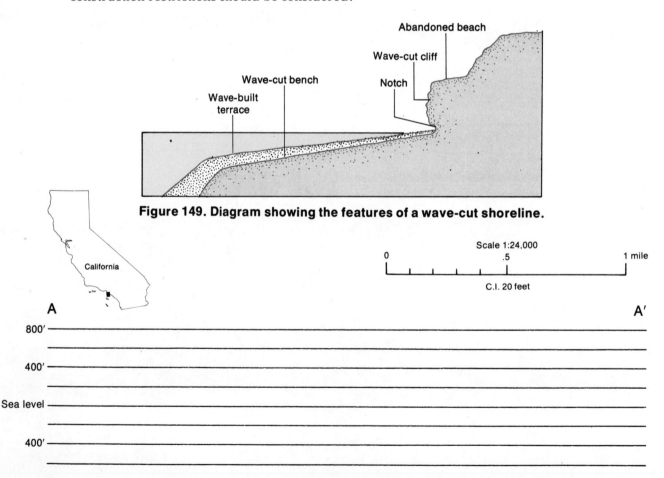

Figure 149. Diagram showing the features of a wave-cut shoreline.

Recent Changes in Shoreline Configuration

Figure 151 (p. 117). Icy Bay, Alaska

In contrast to many geologic regions, coastal areas commonly exhibit marked changes in morphology due to rapid erosion and deposition. As recently as 1904, Icy Bay, on the Gulf of Alaska, was the site of a large glacier which has now retreated approximately 15 miles landward. Marine inundation of Icy Bay has been accompanied by changes in its shoreline configuration caused by longshore drift, and a large spit has formed on the east side of the entrance.

Figure 151 shows Point Riou Spit in 1941, 1957, 1971, and 1975. The spit has not grown continuously; rather, it has advanced and retreated during this relatively short period of time. Recently geologists of the U.S. Geological Survey studied the shoreline changes at Icy Bay because it was being considered as a possible port.

Problems

1. Indicate on each photo where erosion (E) is occurring and where deposition (D) is occurring. Show with arrows the probable path by which sediment is transported to build the spit.

2. What part of the spit appears to have changed most rapidly, the area of erosion or the area of deposition?

3. How will Point Riou Spit probably change in the future?

4. If this area is selected as a harbor, what problems will likely be encountered?

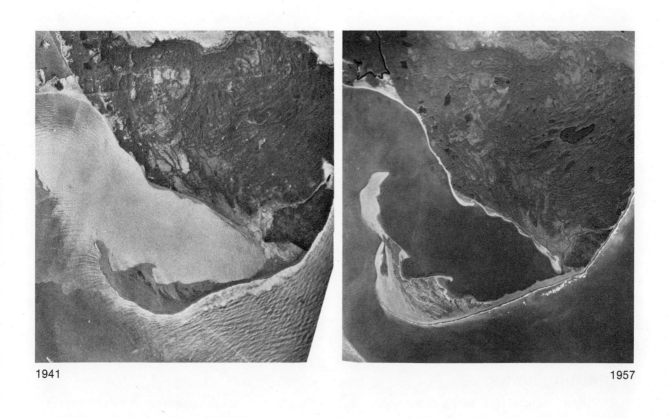

1941   1957

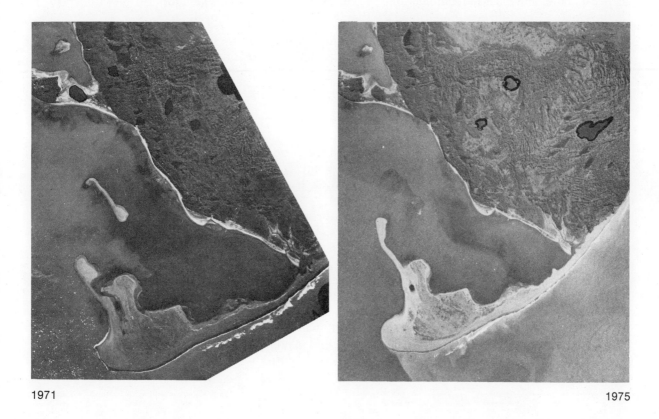

1971   1975

Figure 151. Shoreline changes from 1941 to 1975 at Icy Bay, Alaska.

117

14 Alpine Glaciation

Objective

To recognize the types of landforms developed by alpine glaciers and to understand the processes responsible for their development.

Main Concept

Alpine or valley glaciers are systems of moving ice that flow down preexisting stream valleys. As the ice moves, it erodes the landscape, creating deep U-shaped valleys, sharp interstream divides, cirques, horns, and hanging valleys. Sediment deposited near the end of the glacier typically forms terminal moraines or is reworked by meltwater and deposited as outwash.

Supporting Ideas

1. During a glacial epoch, many thousands of miles of ice flow through systems of valley glaciers and erode the former stream valley by abrasion and glacial plucking.

2. Frost action and mass movement along the valley walls deliver large amounts of rock debris to the glacier. The debris is then transported as lateral and medial moraines.

3. Deposition occurs at the end of the glacier, where the rate of melting exceeds the rate of ice flow. Terminal moraines and outwash plains are major depositional features.

Discussion

The series of diagrams in Figure 152 illustrates how valley glaciers modify a landscape previously sculptured by running water. Prior to glaciation (Figure 152A), the topography is characterized by V-shaped valleys and rounded hills. If one looks up the major valley, spurs or ridges appear to overlap as the stream curves and bends. The size of valleys is proportional to the size of the streams which flow through them. At each stream junction the tributaries join the major streams, without waterfalls or rapids.

During glaciation (Figure 152B), snow fields form in the high mountain ranges and glacier systems expand down the major stream valleys. Glacial erosion by abrasion and plucking, together with frost action, tends to produce sharp, angular landforms. Bowl-shaped depressions called *cirques* develop at the heads of glaciers and erode headward. Where several cirques merge, a sharp, angular peak called a *horn* is produced.

When the glacial period ends and the ice melts (Figure 152C), broad, deep, U-shaped valleys are the most characteristic landform, and cirques, horns, and *arêtes* form spectacular scenery in the highlands. *Hanging valleys*, often with high waterfalls, occur where glacial tributaries entered the main glacier. Debris deposited at the end of the glacier system forms *moraines*, and meltwaters rework glacial sediment to form an *outwash plain* (not shown in the diagram).

Preglaciation

The topography before glaciation is characterized by V-shaped stream valleys, overlapping spurs and rounded hills.

Glaciation

Valley glaciers develop from snowfields in the high peaks and expand down the major stream valleys. Major glaciers, therefore, have a network of tributaries that follow the drainage system.

Postglaciation

Glacial erosion tends to produce sharp, angular landforms. Bowl-shaped depressions called cirques develop at the heads of valleys. Where several cirques merge, a sharp, angular peak called a horn is produced. Divides between glacial valleys develop sharp ridges called arêtes. Valleys that have been glaciated are typically straight and U-shaped in cross section. Major glacial valleys are deep, and spurs are truncated. Glacial tributaries form hanging valleys where they enter the larger glacial valleys. Debris deposited at the end of the glacier forms moraines, and meltwaters rework glacial sediment to form an outwash plain (not shown).

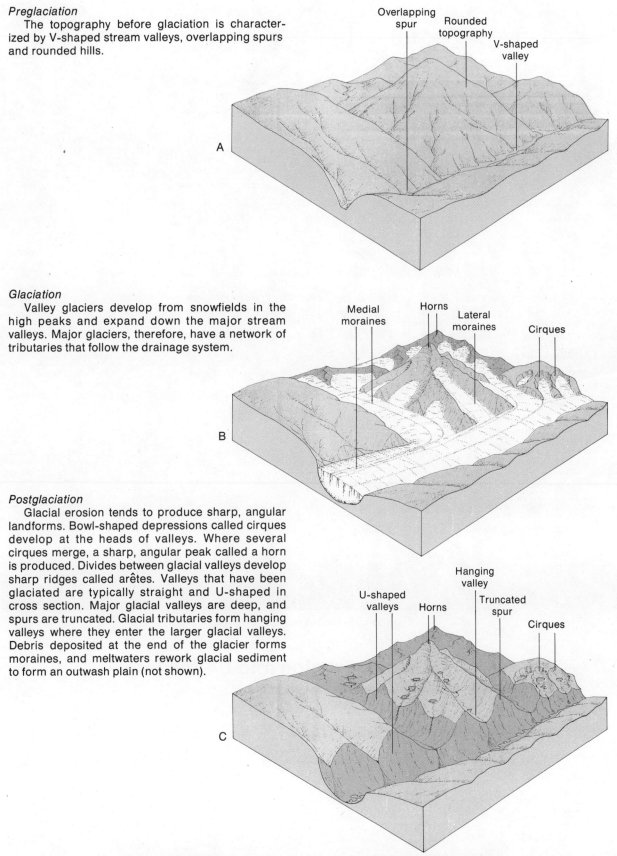

Figure 152. Diagrams of landforms developed by valley glaciers.

119

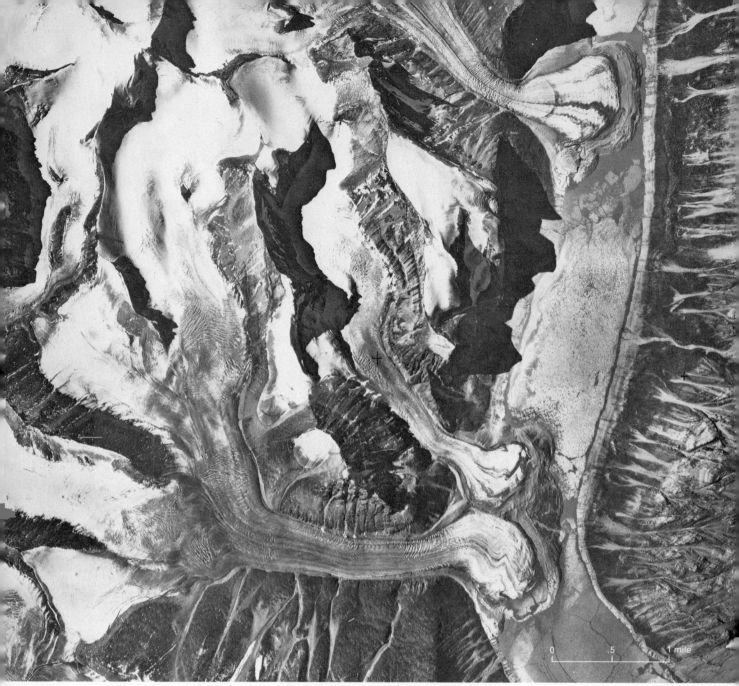

Figure 153. Baffin Island, Canada.

Alpine Glacial Erosion and Deposition

Problems

1. The dark linear streaks on the glacier surface are composed of rock debris. They are called lateral or medial moraines, depending on their location. What is the source of this debris?

2. Are the glaciers advancing or retreating? Cite evidence to support your answer.

3. What evidence is there in this photo to indicate that the glacial ice flows?

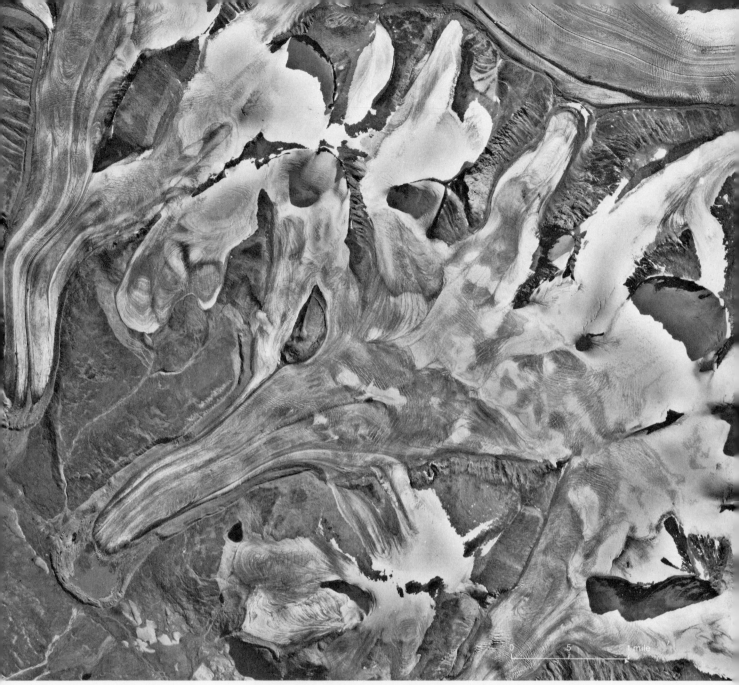

Figure 154. Baffin Island, Canada.

Processes of Alpine Glaciation

Problems

1. Locate and label the major arêtes, horns, and cirques.

2. Study the glacier and note the areas of major crevassing. What causes crevasses to form in a glacier?

3. Trace the margins of each glacier system and indicate areas of accumulation and areas of ablation.

4. Why is a glacier commonly referred to as an "open system"?

5. What evidence do you find that glaciers in this area were once much more extensive than at present?

Processes of Alpine Glaciation

Figure 155 (p. 123). Cordova (C-4), Alaska

The map of Cordova illustrates many active processes of alpine glaciation. The sources of the two major glaciers are northeast of the area shown in the map, but the two glacial fields that cap the mountains' summits feed tributary mountain glaciers which flow to the southwest. The valley of the Rude River and the valley in front of Scott Glacier are more than 2000 feet deep and have the broad, U-shaped cross sections typical of alpine glaciation. Note that valleys are flat floored and steep walled. Compare the contour lines that cross the glacially cut valleys (brown) with the contour lines that cross the present glacier (blue).

Problems

1. Study the landforms and label the following features: (a) outwash plain, (b) arêtes, (c) recessional moraines, (d) medial moraines, (e) hanging valleys, (f) horns, (g) ice crevasses, (h) braided streams, (i) cirques, (j) ice falls.

2. Notice that glaciers, like streams, are fed by tributaries that form a branching pattern. Draw arrows on the map to show the flow of the tributaries to Scott Glacier.

3. Draw a topographic profile across the valley approximately one mile south of the end of Scott Glacier. How does a glacial valley differ from a stream valley?

4. Does it seem reasonable to believe that glaciers can modify the valley through which they flow? What field evidence can you cite to support your answer?

5. Draw a longitudinal profile up Scott Valley to the front of the glacier. If the gradient were projected up the valley under the glacier, what would be the approximate thickness of the ice near the middle of Scott Glacier?

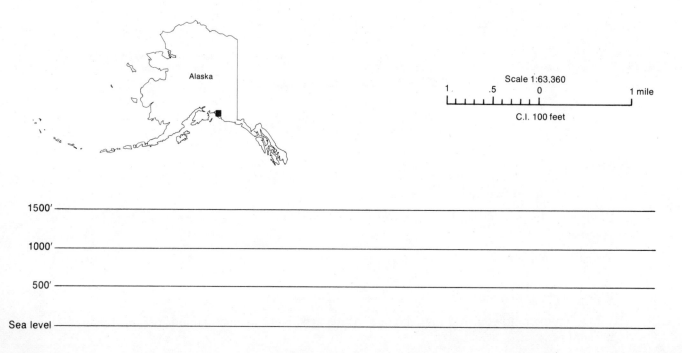

Alaska

Scale 1:63,360

1   .5   0   1 mile

C.I. 100 feet

1500' ——————————————————————

1000' ——————————————————————

500' ——————————————————————

Sea level ——————————————————————

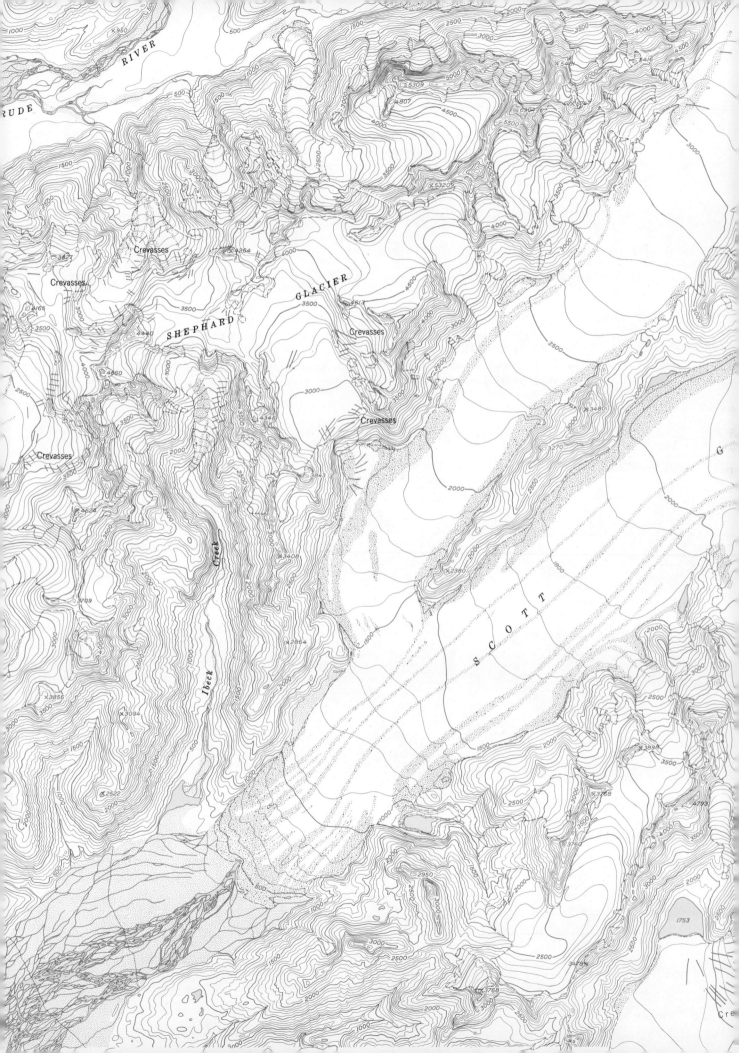

Topography Modified by Alpine Glaciation

Figure 156 (p. 125). Holy Cross, Colorado

During the Ice Age extensive snow fields and alpine glaciers were active in the higher elevations of the Alps and the Himalayas and in the western part of North America. Most of those glaciers have now disappeared or melted into very minor features, leaving a clear depositional and erosional record of their former activity.

The Holy Cross quadrangle of Colorado was extensively glaciated during Pleistocene time in a manner similar to that shown in Figures 153, 154, and 155.

Problems

1. Carefully study the landforms on Figure 156 and color the areas you believe were formerly covered by glaciers.

2. Construct a topographic profile from the southeast margin of the map westward across Turquoise Lake and up Lake Fork Creek. Compare this with the profile you drew for Scott Glacier on the map of Cordova, Alaska. Assume that a valley glacier similar to Scott Glacier once filled this valley. Sketch the glacier on the profile and on the map in order to make a paleogeographic reconstruction.

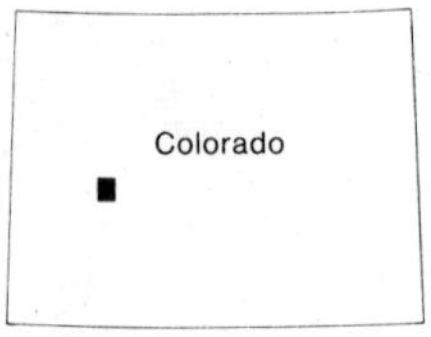

Colorado

Scale 1:62,500

1   .5   0   1 mile

C.I. 50 feet

11,000' ——————————————————————————————————————

10,500' ——————————————————————————————————————

10,000' ——————————————————————————————————————

15 Continental Glaciation

Objective

To recognize the types of landforms developed by continental glaciers and to understand the processes responsible for their development.

Main Concept

A continental glacier is a system of flowing ice, up to 2 miles thick, which moves out from a zone of accumulation and covers the entire landscape. Erosional debris is transported toward the margins of the ice, where it is deposited as a variety of regional landforms.

Supporting Ideas

1. Much of the sediment load is deposited at the ice margins to form terminal moraines.
2. Drumlins, eskers, and ground moraines form beneath the ice.
3. Meltwater from the glacier may transport a considerable amount of glacial debris and deposit it in an outwash plain in front of the ice sheet.

Discussion

Continental glaciers originate in polar regions where there is sufficient precipitation to build up and maintain a thick body of ice. Their margins are irregular or lobate because the advancing ice front flows more rapidly into the lowlands. The thickness of the ice commonly exceeds 10,000 feet. An important result of continental glaciation is that the weight of the ice depresses the earth's crust so that the surrounding land slopes toward the glacier. This produces lakes along the ice margins or permits an arm of the sea to temporarily invade and fill the depression.

Ice Front Stabilized

A number of significant landforms result from geologic processes operating at the margins of continental glaciers, because it is here that the moving ice in the glacier leaves the system by melting and evaporation (Figure 157). Much of the sediment carried by the glacier is therefore deposited along the ice margins or is reworked by meltwater and deposited as *outwash*. The sediment deposited at the ice margins follows the lobate outline of the glacier to form *terminal moraines*, *recessional moraines*, and *interlobate moraines*. Lakes that form in the depression along the ice margins receive sediment from the meltwater, which accumulates as deltas or is dispersed over the lake bottom. Elsewhere, meltwater from the glacier, issuing from tunnels beneath the ice, forms braided streams that deposit stratified fluvial sand and gravel across the *outwash plain*. Blocks of ice broken off from the glacier may become partly buried by sediment in the outwash plain as the glacier begins to recede.

Ice Front Retreated

When the glacier recedes, the ridges of moraines mark the former positions of the ice margins, and well-sorted stratified clay and silt remain at the site of former lakes (Figure 157). The outwash plain is characterized by deposits of fluvial sand and gravel, and depressions known as *kettles* form where partly buried ice blocks have melted. *Ground moraine* is deposited beneath the glacier and may be reshaped into *drumlins* in some localities. Sinuous ridges called *eskers* result from sediment deposited on the floor of former ice tunnels, and numerous lakes fill depressions in the ground moraine. Preglacial drainage has been greatly modified or obliterated.

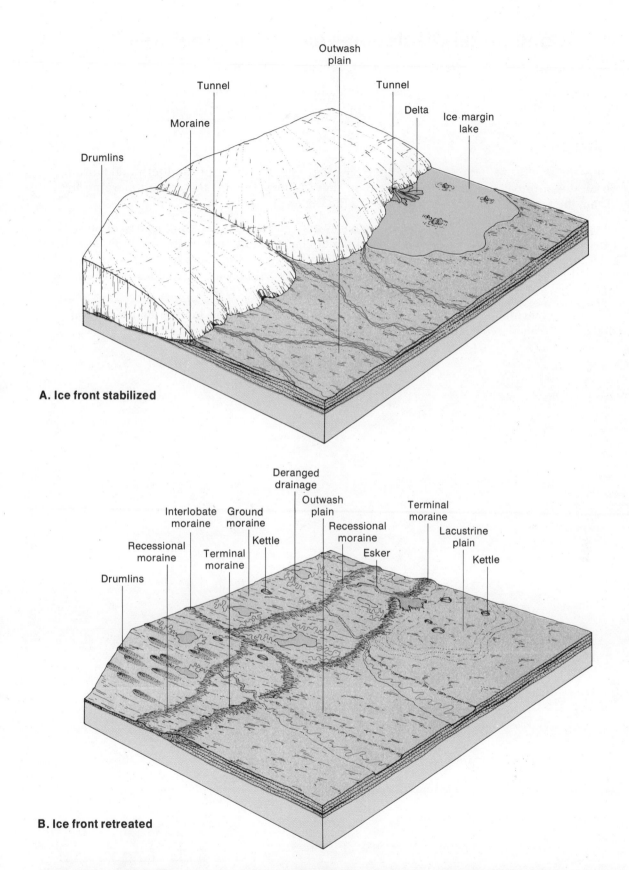

Figure 157. Block diagrams showing landforms developed by continental glaciation. Adapted from A. N. Strahler (1960), *Physical Geography,* New York, John Wiley and Sons.

Continental Glaciation—Ice Margin Features

Figure 158 (p. 129). Jackson, Michigan

The area shown on this map lies just south of the town of Jackson, Michigan. (See also the glacial map, Figure 161).

Problems

1. Study the landforms in this area and identify eskers, ground moraine, and terminal moraine. Draw the approximate boundaries between these features. Color the ground moraine light green, the terminal moraine dark green, and the eskers orange.

2. The poorly developed drainage and extensive swamp and marsh areas on the map of Jackson, Michigan, are typical of areas where continental glaciation has occurred. To emphasize the interconnected and poorly integrated character of this drainage, use a dark blue pencil and trace the drainage system of the Grand River and its tributaries. How does the drainage pattern here compare with the drainage patterns shown in Exercise 9?

3. Is there any evidence from the Jackson drainage pattern that the landforms are primarily depositional and have been only slightly modified by erosion?

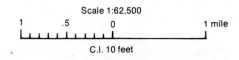

Scale 1:62,500

1   .5   0   1 mile

C.I. 10 feet

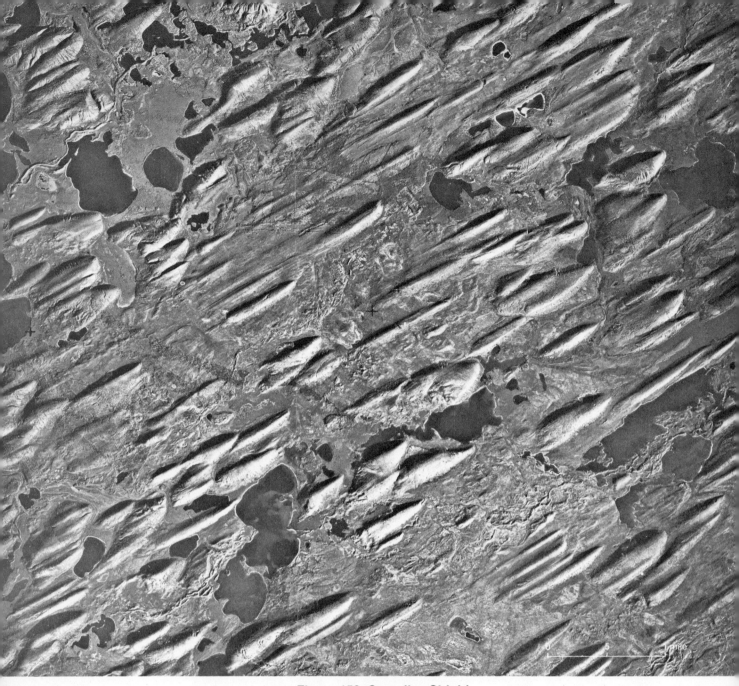

Figure 159. Canadian Shield.

Continental Glaciation—Drumlins

In many regions, unconsolidated, poorly sorted ground moraine deposited by one ice advance is overridden by a subsequent advance and molded into clusters of elliptical hills called drumlins. These streamlined hills typically occur in swarms, with the long axis of the hills parallel to the direction of ice movement.

Problems

1. Show by arrows the direction of the glacier's movement in this area.

2. Consider the shape, orientation, and grouping of the features shown here. Does the assumption that drumlins result from glaciation seem valid?

3. To what extent has stream erosion modified the drumlins?

4. What are the low, sinuous ridges trending roughly parallel to the drumlins?

5. Many cities use sanitary landfills to dispose of solid waste. What problems might arise from using this method of waste disposal in a drumlin area?

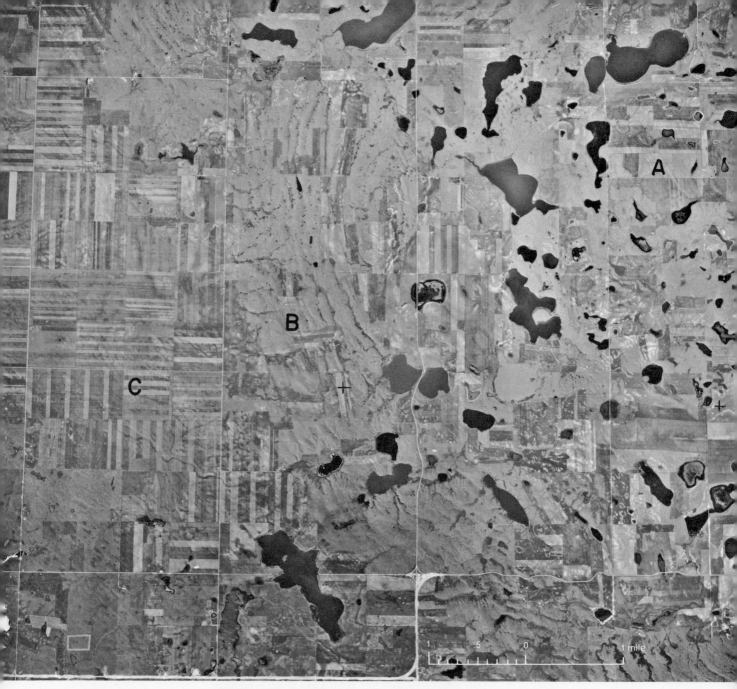

Figure 160. Streeter Moraine, North Dakota.

Continental Glaciation—Ice-Margin Features

The glacial deposits in the Streeter Moraine area include ground moraine, end moraine, and outwash plain.

Problems

1. Draw a line along the contacts between outwash and end moraine and between end moraine and ground moraine. What topographic features characterize each area?

2. What is the origin of the numerous small lakes in the upper right part of the photo?

3. What is the nature and origin of the sediment you might expect to find at points A, B, and C?

4. On the basis of the glacial landforms shown in this photo, construct a generalized paleogeographic map showing the former position of the ice front and indicate the direction of ice movement.

Glacial Map of Parts of Michigan, Ohio, and Indiana

Figure 161 (p. 133). Michigan, Ohio, Indiana

Problems

1. Study the map patterns of the major glacial deposits (outwash, lakes, drift, moraines) and note the contacts of older deposits and younger deposits which are associated with them. On the basis of these relationships determine the relative ages of the following: ground moraine or drift, eskers, outwash sediment, and lake sediments.

2. How many glacial stillstands are represented by the end moraines in Ohio and Indiana along a trend southwest from Lake Erie? Was the glacial front advancing or retreating when these moraines formed?

3. Note the breaks in many of the end moraines. What is the probable cause of the breaks?

4. Study the pattern of outwash sediments (yellow) in the vicinity of the Union City, Mississinewa, Salomie, Wabash, and Fort Wayne moraines (northeastern Indiana). What does this pattern indicate about the direction of drainage during glacial times?

5. What effect did the end moraines have on the location of the glacial lakes that extended beyond the shores of Lake Michigan and Lake Erie, such as Lakes Maumee, Whittlesey, Glenwood, and Calumet?

LEGEND

Lacustrine sediments

Outwash sediments

Ice-contact stratified drift (eskers, kames, etc.)

End moraines of Wisconsin age

Drift, other than end moraines, of Wisconsin age

Drift of Illinoian age

Area not glaciated

WHITTLESEY

Shorelines (beaches, bars, spits, and cliffs)

Striation direction

Streamline features (drumlins, fluted surfaces, etc.)

Outer limit of significant glacial advance

Scale 1:2,500,000

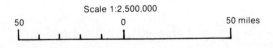

50   0   50 miles

Figure 161

Glacial Map of Part of New England

Figure 162 (p. 135). New England

Problems

1. What was the predominant direction of glacial advance in New England?

2. How do glacial features in this area differ from those shown in Figure 161?

3. How are Long Island, Martha's Vineyard, Nantucket, and Cape Cod related? On the map, sketch the features that once connected these areas but are now submerged.

4. Compare this area with the glacial map of Michigan (Figure 161). What glacial features would you expect to find offshore on the continental shelf?

5. Note the marine deposits along the coast of Maine and in the Champlain Valley. What caused this area to subside and permit marine deposition?

6. In terms of erosion and deposition, what is the major difference between the glaciated regions of New England and of the midcontinent?

LEGEND

Marine sediments

Lacustrine sediments

Outwash sediments

Ice-contact stratified drift (eskers, kames, etc.)

End moraines of Wisconsin age

Drift, other than end moraines, of Wisconsin age

Drift of Illinoian age

Drift of Kansan age

Area not glaciated

Striation direction

Streamline features (drumlins, fluted surfaces, etc.)

Scale 1:2,500,000

50   0   50 miles

Figure 162

16 Structural Geology

Objective

To become acquainted with the major structural features of the earth's crust and the outcrop patterns they produce and to understand what each major feature implies about the mobility of the crust.

Main Concept

Each major geologic structure, such as an anticline, syncline, dome, basin, or fault, has a specific geometric form and when exposed at the earth's surface produces distinctive outcrop patterns that can be recognized on an aerial photo or geologic map.

Supporting Ideas

1. A geologic map shows the distribution of rock formations, faults, and other structural features as they are exposed at the earth's surface. It is a scale model of the rock bodies of the crust and a fundamental tool for analyzing and interpreting geologic data.
2. From careful analysis of a geologic map and/or an aerial photo, one can interpret a region's geologic history.

Discussion

It is very important for a student of geology to obtain an accurate idea of the size, shape, and areal extent of rock bodies. Units of sandstone, limestone, or shale, which are called formations, may range from a few feet to several thousand feet in thickness and may cover an area of more than 200,000 square miles. Formations, therefore, exist as extensive layers of rock which may cover several states. Throughout their extent, they may be warped into folds, displaced by faults, and dissected by erosion.

The problem of studying the distribution and structure of rock bodies is similar to the problem of studying the distribution of land and water; it is basically a problem of scale. For example, it is impossible to conceive of the Mississippi River with all its tributaries by looking at it from one place or even several hundred places. In order to form an accurate conception of so large a feature as a complete river system, it is necessary to make a detailed survey and construct hydrographic maps. The same is true of rock formations: an understanding of the configuration and areal extent of an entire rock body can be obtained only by careful mapping. Geologic maps provide a regional picture of the geometry of rock bodies and a unique perspective from which to analyze structural relationships. The geologic map is thus a fundamental tool for geologic research.

In order to understand the surface expression of structural features it is necessary first to review the basic three-dimensional geometry of the major structural types.

Folds

Regional tectonic forces commonly deform rocks into a series of folds so that rocks which were originally horizontal are tilted, twisted, and bent. In order to analyze this type of deformation, geologists recognize several basic types of structures, some of which are illustrated in Figures 163 and 164.

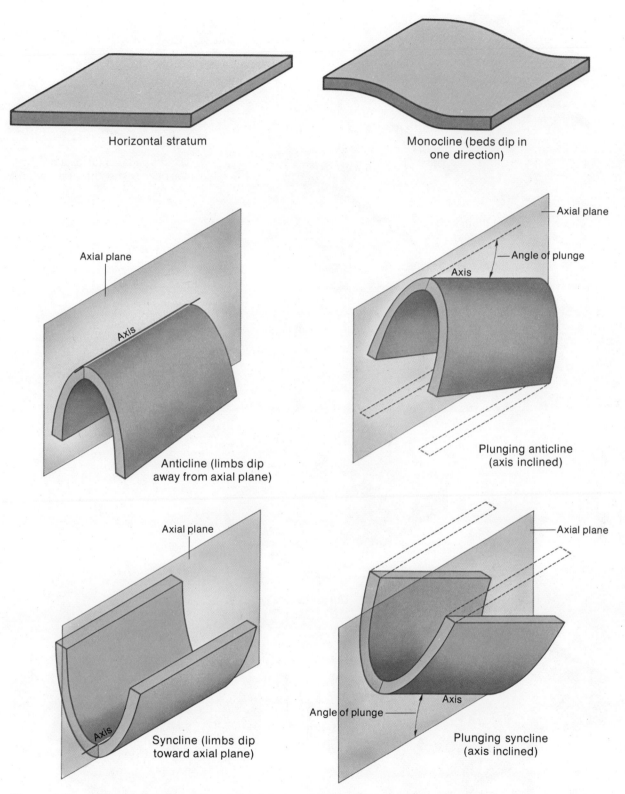

Horizontal stratum

Monocline (beds dip in one direction)

Axial plane

Axis

Anticline (limbs dip away from axial plane)

Axial plane

Axis

Angle of plunge

Plunging anticline (axis inclined)

Axial plane

Axis

Syncline (limbs dip toward axial plane)

Axial plane

Axis

Angle of plunge

Plunging syncline (axis inclined)

Figure 163. The geometry and nomenclature of folds. The geometry of folds is described with reference to the axial plane and the axis. The *axial plane* is an imaginary plane dividing the fold into two equal parts. The *fold axis* is a line made by the intersection of the axial plane and the bedding plane. Most folds are not horizontal over long distances but are inclined, and the fold is said to plunge. The plunge of a fold is measured by the direction and amount of downward inclination of the axis.

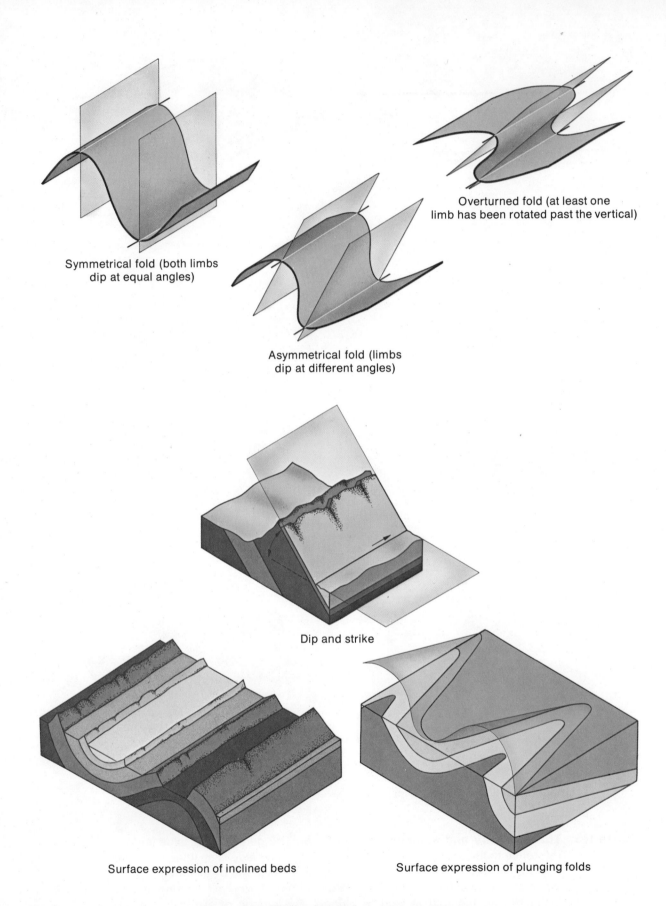

Symmetrical fold (both limbs
dip at equal angles)

Asymmetrical fold (limbs
dip at different angles)

Overturned fold (at least one
limb has been rotated past the vertical)

Dip and strike

Surface expression of inclined beds

Surface expression of plunging folds

Figure 164. Folds and their outcrop patterns.

Faults

Tectonic forces do not always cause the development of folded sequences. Instead, the rocks may break or fracture, and frequently movement occurs along the fracture surface. This type of deformation is referred to as *faulting*. The surface along which movement takes place is a *fault plane*. The block above the fault plane is called the *hanging wall* and the block below it is the *footwall*. The major types of faults are illustrated in Figure 165.

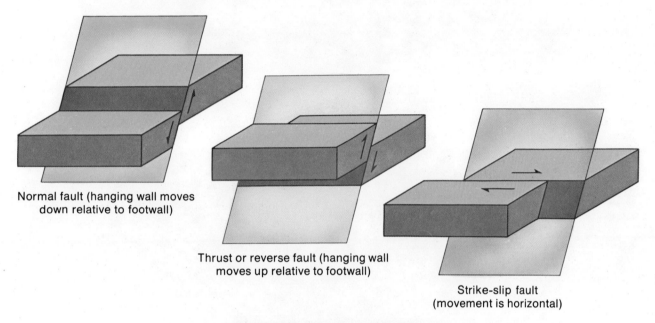

Normal fault (hanging wall moves down relative to footwall)

Thrust or reverse fault (hanging wall moves up relative to footwall)

Strike-slip fault (movement is horizontal)

Figure 165. The geometry of faults.

Block Diagrams and Geologic Maps of Major Structural Types

A geologic map shows the distribution of rock units as they crop out at the surface of the earth. Each unit is shown by various colors or in tones of gray. Symbols showing the dip and strike of sedimentary strata and the presence of faults and folds are also included. A legend accompanies the map to define the symbols and indicate the ages and stratigraphic relationships of rock units. The conventional symbols for common structural features are shown in Figure 166.

The major types of structural features produce distinctive patterns on geologic maps and can be easily recognized. Examples of various common structural patterns are shown in Figures 167 through 176. In each figure a block diagram shows a bird's-eye view of the structural features and their topographic expression. The outcrop pattern of each rock unit shown on the block diagram is projected onto a horizontal plane to represent a geologic map shown in perspective. This arrangement makes it easy to relate the structure shown on the block diagram to the map patterns.

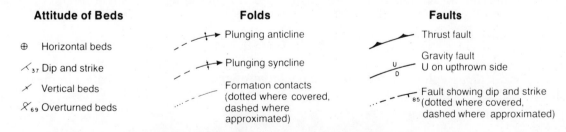

Attitude of Beds

⊕ Horizontal beds

$\diagup_{37}$ Dip and strike

$\diagup$ Vertical beds

$\diagup_{69}$ Overturned beds

Folds

Plunging anticline

Plunging syncline

Formation contacts (dotted where covered, dashed where approximated)

Faults

Thrust fault

Gravity fault
U on upthrown side

Fault showing dip and strike (dotted where covered, dashed where approximated)

Figure 166. Geologic map symbols.

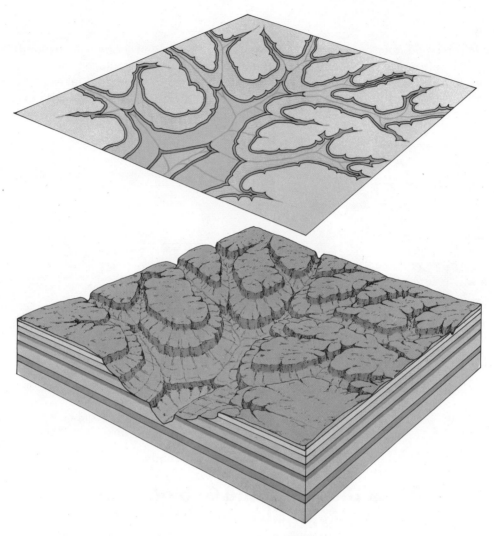

Figure 167. Block diagram and geologic map showing outcrop pattern of horizontal strata.

Outcrop Pattern of Horizontal Strata

Dendritic drainage patterns characteristically develop on horizontal strata and cut canyons or valleys. Progressively older rock units are exposed as the canyons deepen. As a result, the map patterns of horizontal strata parallel stream valleys and produce a dendritic pattern on the geologic map. The contacts of rock units of horizontal strata parallel the topographic contour lines. Escarpments and gentle slopes generally develop on resistant and nonresistant beds, respectively, and thus produce variations in the width of the map outcrop patterns. On steep cliffs the upper and lower contacts (as seen on the map) will be close together, whereas on a gentle slope of the same formation the contacts will appear farther apart. It is apparent, therefore, that the map width of the outcrop belts of horizontal strata is not dependent solely on the units' thickness.

Gently dipping strata will develop the same basic outcrop pattern as horizontal beds. However, the contacts between rock units in gently dipping strata, when traced far enough up a valley, cross topographic contours and form a large V-shaped pattern that points in the direction the beds dip.

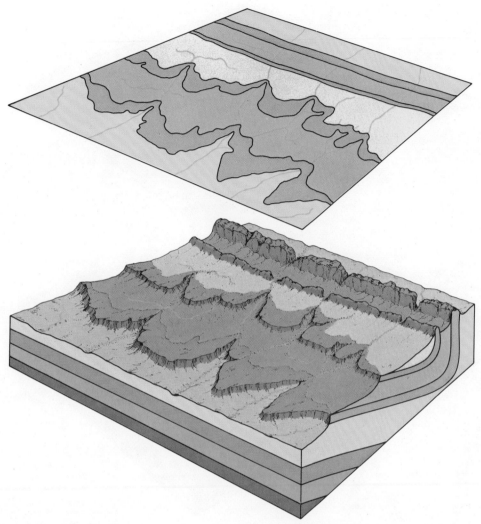

Figure 168. Block diagram and geologic map showing outcrop pattern of inclined strata.

Outcrop Pattern of Inclined Strata

When a sequence of rocks is tilted and truncated by erosion, the outcrop patterns appear as bands that, seen on a regional scale, are roughly parallel. Important variations in details of the basic pattern develop in areas dissected by erosion. These variations should be carefully analyzed, for they provide important information about the subsurface structure. When dipping strata are traced across a valley, a V-shaped outcrop pattern that points in the direction of the dip is produced. An exception to the rule is possible if the degree of bedding dip is less than the gradient of the valley, but such a condition is seldom encountered. The size of the outcrop-pattern V is inversely proportional to the magnitude of the dip:

1. Low-angle dip, large V (front of Figure 168)
2. High-angle dip, small V
3. Vertical dip, no V (back of Figure 168)

Careful study of Figure 168 will reveal several more relationships basic to geologic maps:

1. Older beds dip toward younger beds unless the sequence is overturned.
2. Outcrop width depends on (a) the thickness of the beds, (b) the dip of the beds (the lower the dip, the wider the outcrop), and (c) the slope of the topography (the steeper the slope, the narrower the outcrop).

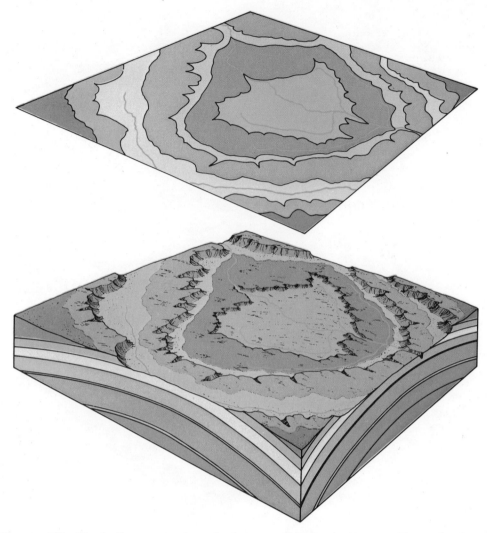

Figure 169. Block diagram and geologic map showing outcrop pattern of a dome.

Outcrop Pattern of Domes

Eroded, dome-shaped structures form a roughly circular to elliptical outcrop with beds dipping away from the crest. Domes range in size from small warps a few feet in diameter to regional features covering hundreds or thousands of square miles. As can be seen in Figure 169, the central part of an eroded dome is made up of the oldest bed, and progressively younger rocks are located outward from the center of the structure.

Drainage patterns are helpful in interpreting domal structures because (1) secondary streams tend to form a circular pattern on the less resistant beds and (2) streams cutting across the resistant beds permit one to apply the rule of Vs to determine the direction of dip. If the relative ages of rock units are shown on the map, a dome is easily identified because the older rocks are in the center of the structure.

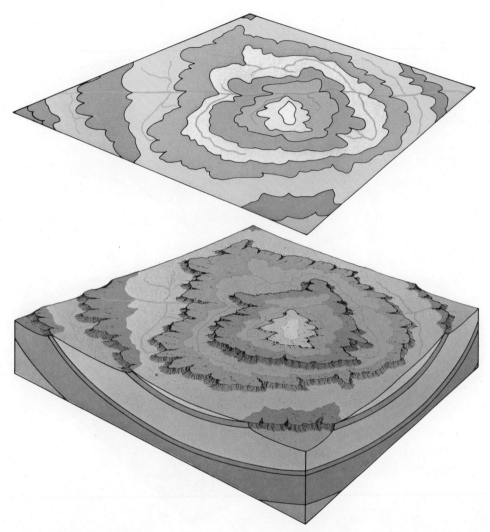

Figure 170. Block diagram and geologic map showing outcrop pattern of a basin.

Outcrop Pattern of Basins

A structural basin, when eroded and exposed on the earth's surface, displays an outcrop pattern very similar to that of an eroded dome. Two major features, however, distinguish a basin from a dome: (1) younger rocks crop out in the center of a basin and older rocks in the center of a dome and (2) if the structure has been dissected by stream erosion, the outcrop Vs point toward the center of a basin and away from the center of a dome.

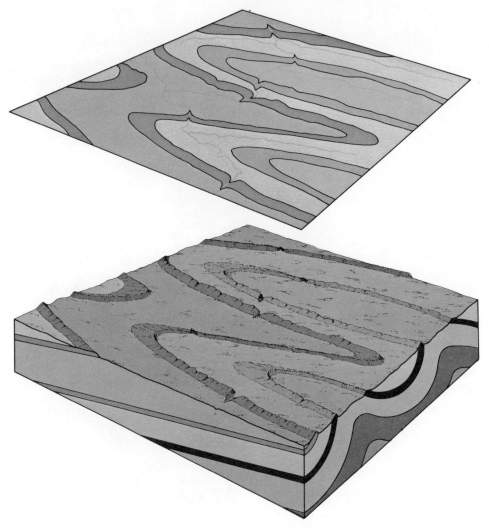

Figure 171. Block diagram and geologic map showing outcrop pattern of plunging folds.

Outcrop Pattern of Plunging Folds

Folding is one of the most common types of structural deformation. It is found in complex mountain ranges and in lowlands and plateaus.

A convex upward fold, or anticline, has limbs that dip away from the axis. In eroded anticlines the oldest rocks are exposed in the core, or center. Synclines are folds that are concave upward, with limbs dipping toward the axis. Eroded synclines have the youngest rocks exposed in the center.

In some folds the axis is horizontal, but more commonly it is inclined and the fold plunges. Plunging folds which have been truncated by erosion form a characteristic zigzag outcrop pattern. A plunging anticline forms a V-shaped outcrop pattern with the apex (or nose) pointing in the direction of the plunge. Plunging synclines form a similar pattern, but the limbs of the fold open in the direction of plunge.

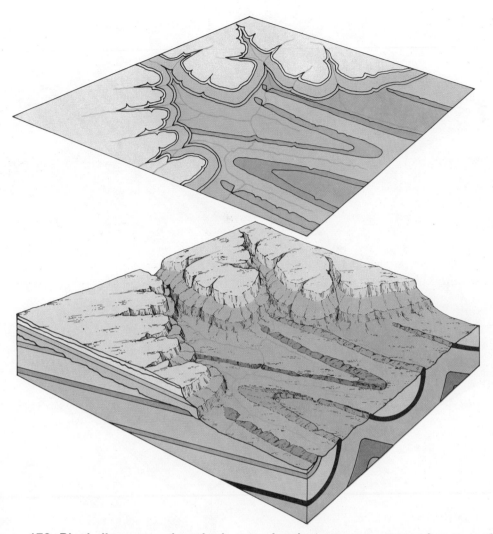

Figure 172. Block diagram and geologic map showing outcrop pattern of an unconformity.

Outcrop Pattern of Angular Unconformities

Angular unconformities can be recognized on geologic maps by interruptions or discontinuities in the outcrop patterns in which older structural trends are partly covered by younger strata. Contacts of the older structures will thus abruptly terminate against the patterns of the overlying younger beds. In Figure 172, the oldest sequence has been warped into plunging folds, eroded, and subsequently covered by a younger sequence of strata. A second period of erosion has partly removed the younger strata and exposed segments of the folds. The angular unconformity is located at the base of the sequence of younger, horizontal strata. *All of the map patterns of the older strata terminate against this contact.* Vs in the trace of the unconformable surface indicate the direction in which it dips. Angular unconformities indicate major events in the geologic history of a region and are therefore extremely important in the interpretation of geologic maps.

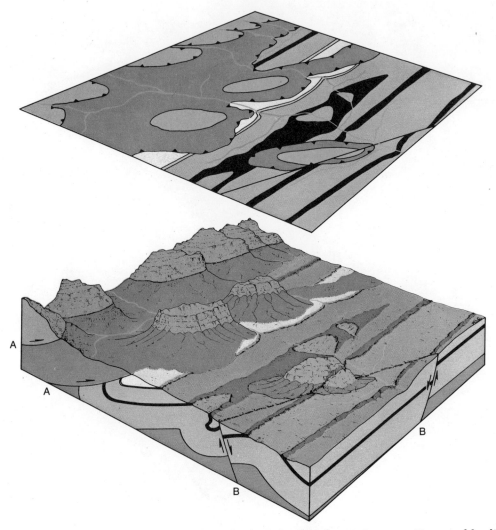

Figure 173. Block diagram and geologic map showing outcrop patterns of faults.

Outcrop Pattern of Faults

Fault patterns on geologic maps are distinctive in that they abruptly offset structures and terminate contacts. They are expressed on the geologic map by heavy lines so they can be recognized easily.

Thrust faults (see point A in Figure 173) generally dip at a low angle, and the stratigraphic displacement that results is usually measured in miles. Because the dip of thrust faults is generally at a low angle, the pattern of the fault trace is characteristically irregular and similar in many respects to that produced by low-dipping angular unconformities (compare Figures 172 and 173). The trace of the thrust commonly forms Vs across valleys, which point in the direction the fault dips. Erosion may form windows (fensters) through the thrust sheet or produce isolated remnants (klippen) in front of the thrust block. Hachures are used to designate the overthrust block.

Because normal and reverse faults usually dip at a high angle, their outcrop patterns are relatively straight (see point B in Figure 173). If the fault plane is slightly inclined, small Vs form across valleys and point in the direction of dip. Since older rocks are generally exposed on the upthrown block, it is possible to determine the relative movement on most high-angle faults from the map relations alone.

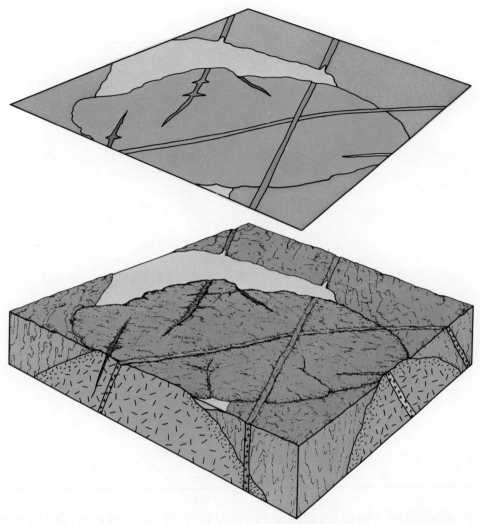

Figure 174. Block diagram and geologic map showing outcrop pattern of intrusive rocks.

Outcrop Pattern of Intrusive Rocks

Intrusive igneous bodies may be either concordant or discordant with the surrounding stratified rocks. The larger intrusives, such as stocks and batholiths, are characteristically discordant and elliptical. Their outcrop patterns appear on geologic maps as elliptical or roughly circular areas that cut across the contacts of the surrounding formations. Smaller discordant intrusives, such as dikes, are characteristically tabular. Dikes generally follow joint or fault systems and appear on geologic maps as straight, usually short, bands. Some dikes, however, are lenticular and appear so on the map.

Concordant igneous bodies, such as sills and laccoliths, have contacts parallel to those of the surrounding rock formations.

The relative age of igneous bodies can be recognized on a geologic map from the cross-cutting contacts: the younger intrusives cut the older.

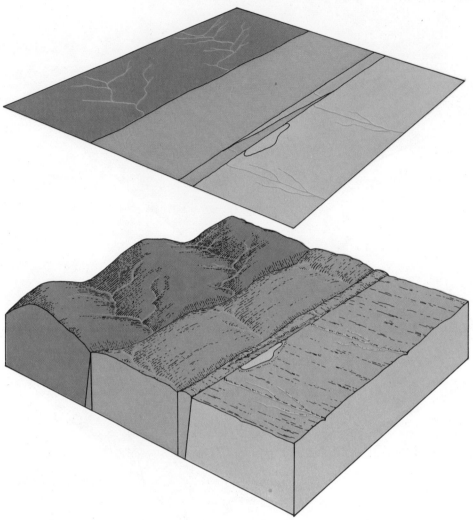

Figure 175. Block diagram and geologic map showing surface features produced by strike-slip faults.

Outcrop Pattern of Strike-Slip Faults

A strike-slip fault is a fault in which the displacement is parallel to the strike of the fault plane. This type of displacement results from horizontal stress in the lithosphere and is commonly associated with spreading of an oceanic ridge. Displacement on strike-slip faults may reach several hundred miles, so that rock types of very different structures and geologic characteristics may be placed side by side. The trend of strike-slip faults is typically straight, in contrast to the irregular trace of thrust faults and the zigzag trace of normal faults.

The lateral displacement of the crust in strike-slip faults does not produce high scarps, but the fault line is commonly marked by structural and topographic discontinuities, linear ridges and valleys, and offset drainage patterns.

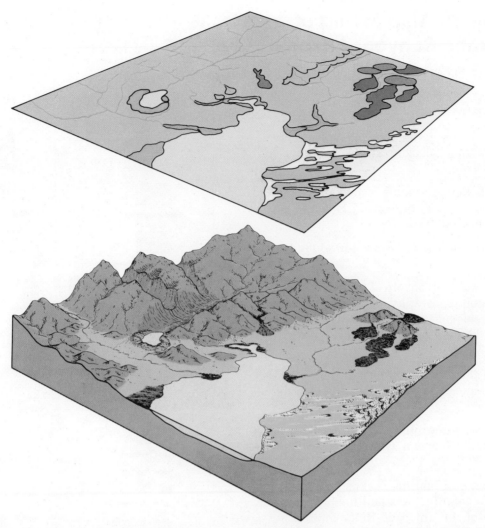

Figure 176. Block diagram and geologic map showing outcrop pattern of surficial deposits.

Outcrop Pattern of Surficial Deposits

Surficial deposits are recent accumulations of various types of sediment or volcanic debris on the surface of the landscape. They are charcteristically thin and generally mask the underlying rock units. The principal types of surficial deposits include windblown sand and loess, stream channel and flood plain deposits, landslide deposits, glacial deposits, and beaches and other shoreline sediments.

On a geologic map recent surficial deposits typically form an elongate, irregular pattern commonly associated with stream valleys (note the location of lava and fluvial deposits in Figure 176). They rest unconformably upon the underlying bedrock and do not extend into the subsurface.

Geologic Map of Part of the Grand Canyon, Arizona

Figure 177 (p. 151). Grand Canyon

Problems

1. How do the outcrop patterns indicate that most of the Paleozoic strata in this area are horizontal?

2. What is the approximate thickness of the Paleozoic strata in the area? How did you arrive at your answer?

3. Draw a geologic cross section along line A-A'.

4. Notice the relationship of rock type to cliff and slope topography on the map and on your geologic cross section. Which rock types develop cliffs and which develop slopes?

5. Notice the outcrop pattern of the Temple Butte Limestone. Why is this pattern discontinuous?

6. How many unconformities are shown on this map? Between what units are they located?

7. What type of faulting is expressed on the map? What effect has faulting had on the course of the Colorado River and on the development of tributary valleys?

8. Two sets of faults are shown on this map, one trending northwest and the other northeast. Which set is the older?

Scale 1:62,500

1   .5   0   1 mile

C.I. 50 feet

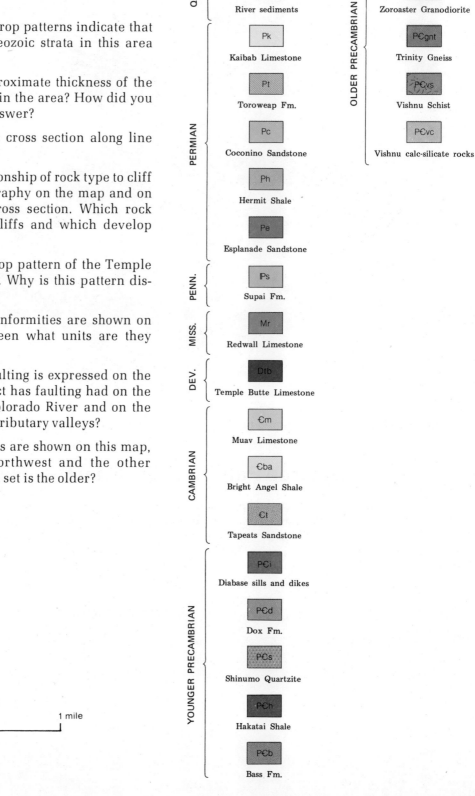

LEGEND

QUATERNARY

S — Landslides and rockfalls

r — River sediments

PERMIAN

Pk — Kaibab Limestone

Pt — Toroweap Fm.

Pc — Coconino Sandstone

Ph — Hermit Shale

Pe — Esplanade Sandstone

PENN.

Ps — Supai Fm.

MISS.

Mr — Redwall Limestone

DEV.

Dtb — Temple Butte Limestone

CAMBRIAN

Cm — Muav Limestone

Cba — Bright Angel Shale

Ct — Tapeats Sandstone

YOUNGER PRECAMBRIAN

PCi — Diabase sills and dikes

PCd — Dox Fm.

PCs — Shinumo Quartzite

PCh — Hakatai Shale

PCb — Bass Fm.

OLDER PRECAMBRIAN

PCgr₁ — Zoroaster Granite

PCgr₂ — Zoroaster Granodiorite

PCgnt — Trinity Gneiss

PCvs — Vishnu Schist

PCvc — Vishnu calc-silicate rocks

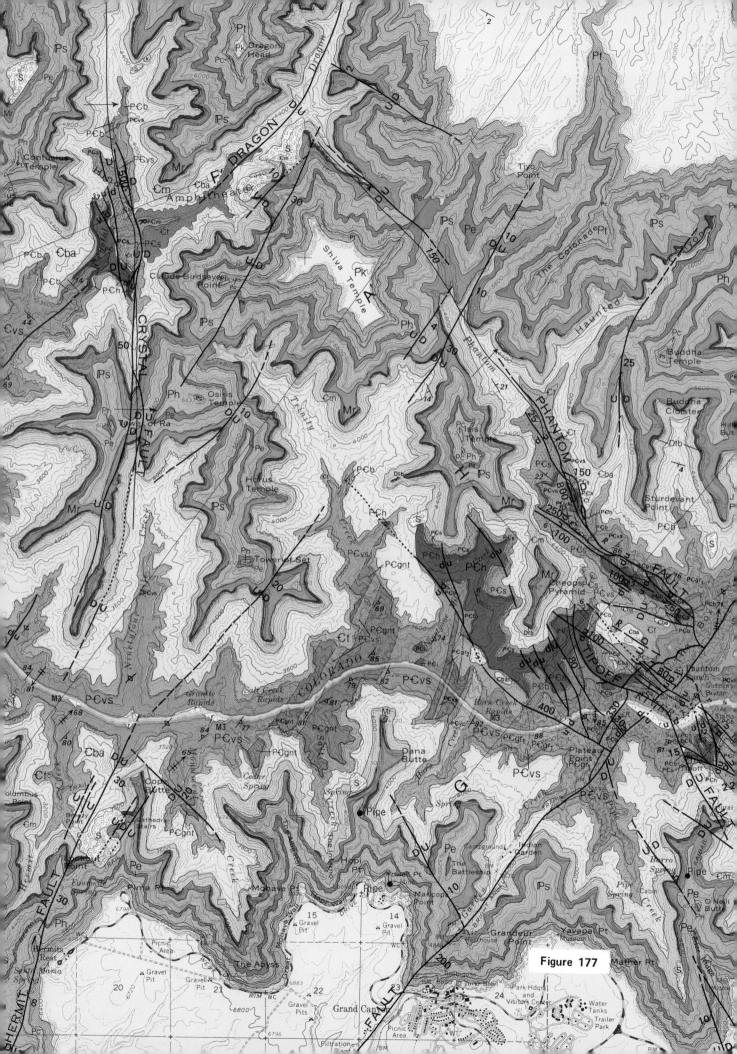

Figure 177

Geologic Map of Michigan and the Surrounding Area

Figure 178 (p. 153). Michigan and surrounding area

Problems

1. Where are the youngest rocks exposed in this area?

2. Study the patterns made by the rock units in Michigan and the adjacent area. What major structural feature is shown?

3. Note the age of the units deformed in this structure. What is the oldest age assignable to the deformation?

4. Assuming that the units on this map dip at a low angle, sketch an east-west geologic cross section through the center of Michigan.

5. Note the outcrop pattern of the lower Paleozoic rocks (Ordovician and Devonian) and that of the upper Paleozoic rocks (Carboniferous) in the area around the Illinois-Indiana state line. What major structural feature is present in this area?

6. What type of fault is present south of Saginaw Bay? What was the relative movement—north side up or down?

7. What major unconformities occur in the rock sequence in this area?

LEGEND

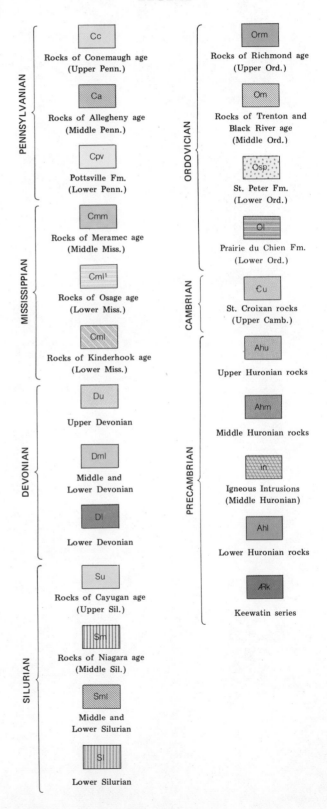

PENNSYLVANIAN

Cc — Rocks of Conemaugh age (Upper Penn.)

Ca — Rocks of Allegheny age (Middle Penn.)

Cpv — Pottsville Fm. (Lower Penn.)

MISSISSIPPIAN

Cmm — Rocks of Meramec age (Middle Miss.)

Cml¹ — Rocks of Osage age (Lower Miss.)

Cml — Rocks of Kinderhook age (Lower Miss.)

DEVONIAN

Du — Upper Devonian

Dml — Middle and Lower Devonian

Dl — Lower Devonian

SILURIAN

Su — Rocks of Cayugan age (Upper Sil.)

Sm — Rocks of Niagara age (Middle Sil.)

Sml — Middle and Lower Silurian

Sl — Lower Silurian

ORDOVICIAN

Orm — Rocks of Richmond age (Upper Ord.)

Om — Rocks of Trenton and Black River age (Middle Ord.)

Osp — St. Peter Fm. (Lower Ord.)

Ol — Prairie du Chien Fm. (Lower Ord.)

CAMBRIAN

Cu — St. Croixan rocks (Upper Camb.)

PRECAMBRIAN

Ahu — Upper Huronian rocks

Ahm — Middle Huronian rocks

in — Igneous Intrusions (Middle Huronian)

Ahl — Lower Huronian rocks

ARk — Keewatin series

Scale 1:2,500,000

50   0   50 miles

Figure 178

Geologic Map
of the Wyoming Area

Figure 179 (p. 155). Wyoming

Problems

1. Study the outcrop pattern in the northeast corner of the map. This area is the Black Hills of South Dakota and Wyoming. Describe the geologic structure.

2. What is the age of the oldest beds in the center of this structure?

3. Is this structure symmetrical or asymmetrical? What facts led you to this answer?

4. Draw a geologic cross section along an east-west line through the center of this structure, showing all beds in both the surface and the subsurface.

5. Judging from the outcrop pattern of Φw on the east flank of this structure, what would be the age of deformation in this area?

6. Are the intrusions older or younger than the deformation of the sedimentary rocks in this area? What map patterns support your answer?

7. What major structure is located between the Black Hills and Buffalo, Wyoming?

8. Study the outcrops of Precambrian rock. What structures are associated with these outcrops?

9. Study the outcrops of Tertiary rocks in Wyoming. What structures are associated with these outcrops?

10. Using a red pencil, complete the geologic map by drawing the axes of the major domes and basins.

11. Study the outcrop patterns of Φw throughout Wyoming. What do they tell you about the age of deformation of the Rocky Mountains?

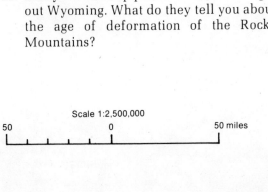

Scale 1:2,500,000

50   0   50 miles

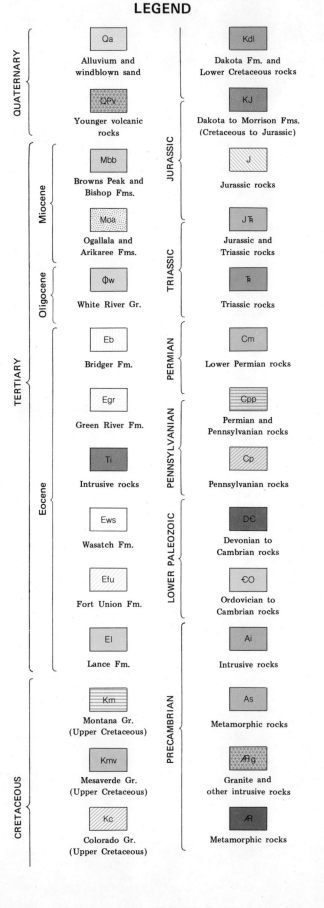

LEGEND

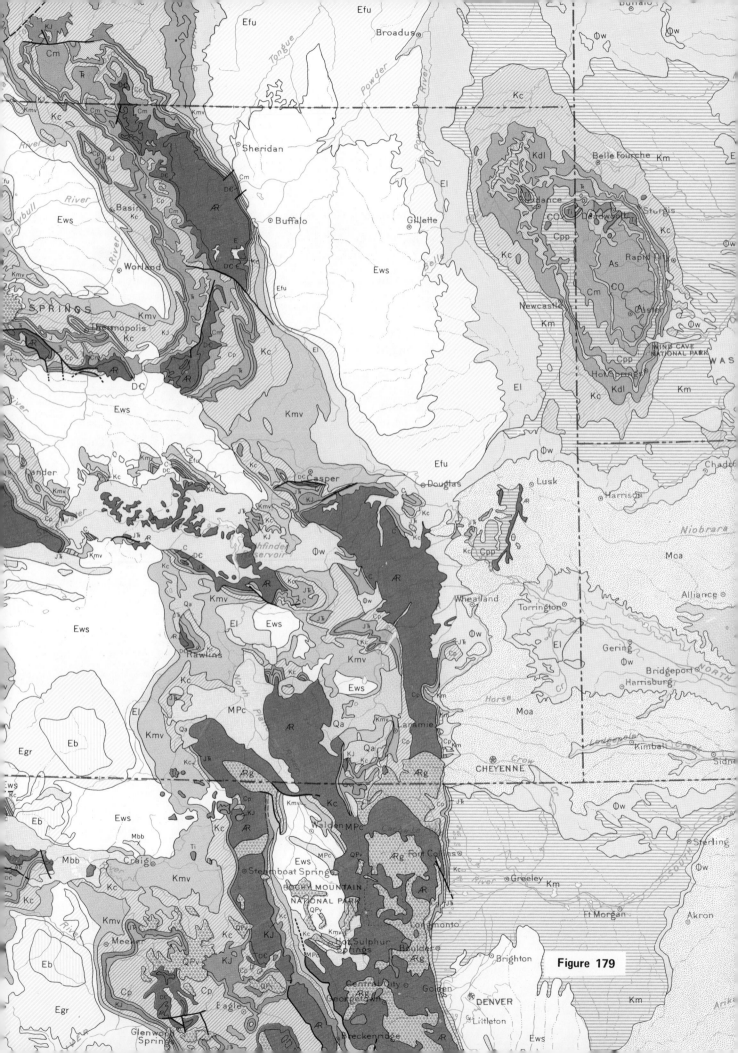

Figure 179

Geologic Map of the Southern States

Figure 180 (p. 157). Southern states

Problems

1. What is the regional strike of the Cretaceous and Tertiary rocks in southern Alabama?

2. In what direction do these rocks dip?

3. What is the regional strike of the Paleozoic rocks in Tennessee, Georgia, and northeastern Alabama?

4. What structural features are indicated by the outcrop patterns of these Paleozoic rocks?

5. What is the structural relationship of the Cretaceous rocks and the underlying Paleozoic rocks? What is the sequence of events which produced this relationship?

6 If you were to divide the area into geologic regions, where would you draw the boundaries between major provinces? On what factors did you base your decision?

7. Outline a sequence of events for the area to account for the differences in outcrop patterns and age relationships.

8. Are the faults in eastern Tennessee normal or thrust?

9. From the structural trend of the Paleozoic rocks, determine the orientation of forces responsible for pre-Cretaceous deformation.

10. What structural feature dominates the northwest quarter of the map?

Scale 1:2,500,000

50   0   50 miles

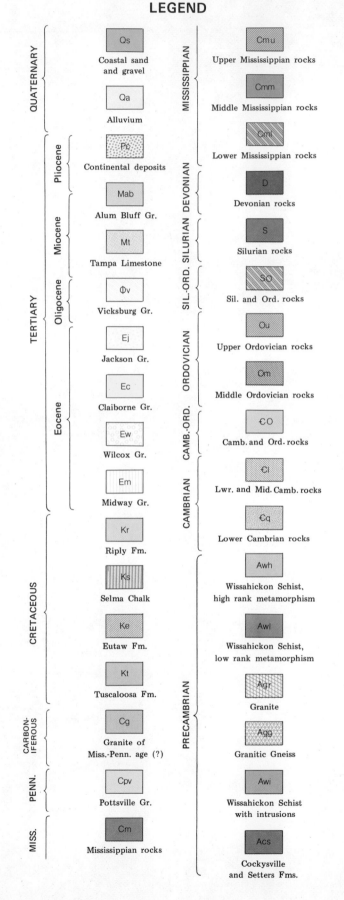

LEGEND

QUATERNARY
- Qs — Coastal sand and gravel
- Qa — Alluvium

TERTIARY

Pliocene
- Pc — Continental deposits

Miocene
- Mab — Alum Bluff Gr.
- Mt — Tampa Limestone

Oligocene
- Ov — Vicksburg Gr.

Eocene
- Ej — Jackson Gr.
- Ec — Claiborne Gr.
- Ew — Wilcox Gr.
- Em — Midway Gr.

CRETACEOUS
- Kr — Riply Fm.
- Ks — Selma Chalk
- Ke — Eutaw Fm.
- Kt — Tuscaloosa Fm.

CARBONIFEROUS
- Cg — Granite of Miss.-Penn. age (?)

PENN.
- Cpv — Pottsville Gr.

MISS.
- Cm — Mississippian rocks

MISSISSIPPIAN
- Cmu — Upper Mississippian rocks
- Cmm — Middle Mississippian rocks
- Cml — Lower Mississippian rocks

SIL.-ORD. SILURIAN DEVONIAN
- D — Devonian rocks
- S — Silurian rocks
- SO — Sil. and Ord. rocks

ORDOVICIAN
- Ou — Upper Ordovician rocks
- Om — Middle Ordovician rocks

CAMB.-ORD.
- CO — Camb. and Ord. rocks

CAMBRIAN
- Ci — Lwr. and Mid. Camb. rocks
- Cq — Lower Cambrian rocks

PRECAMBRIAN
- Awh — Wissahickon Schist, high rank metamorphism
- Awl — Wissahickon Schist, low rank metamorphism
- Agr — Granite
- Agg — Granitic Gneiss
- Awi — Wissahickon Schist with intrusions
- Acs — Cockysville and Setters Fms.

156

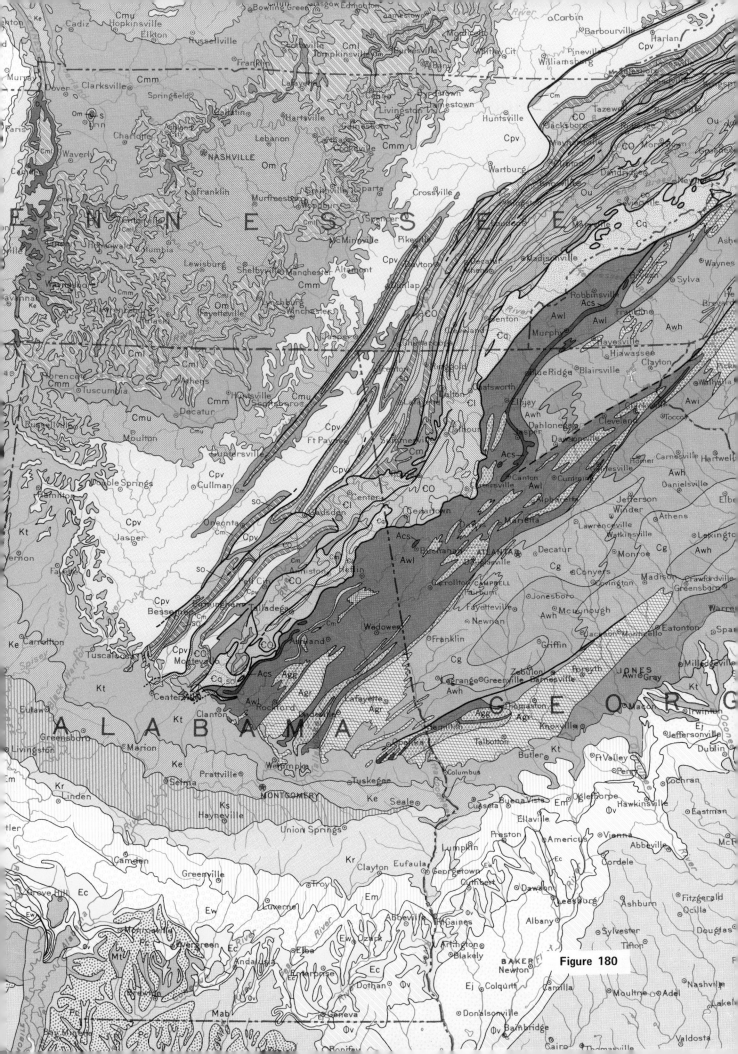

Figure 180

Geologic Map of Mount Eisenhower, Alberta, Canada

Figure 181 (p. 159). Mount Eisenhower

Problems

1. Locate the major thrust faults in the area. How are they related to the folds?

2. Judging from the outcrop pattern of the thrust faults, would you consider them high-angle or low-angle faults?

3. Consider the age of the youngest deformed beds. What would be the age of the orogenic event that produced the thrusting?

4. Look at the symbols used by the Geological Survey of Canada for normal faults. Are the normal faults in the southwest corner of the map older or younger than the thrusts?

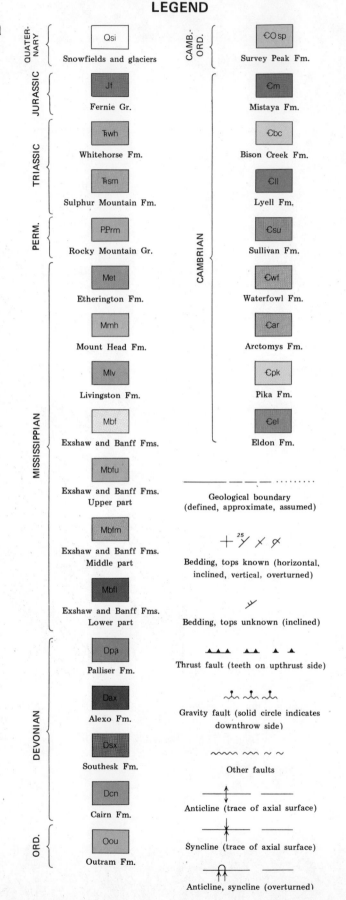

LEGEND

QUATERNARY
- Qsi — Snowfields and glaciers

JURASSIC
- Jf — Fernie Gr.

TRIASSIC
- ℞wh — Whitehorse Fm.
- ℞sm — Sulphur Mountain Fm.

PERM.
- PPrm — Rocky Mountain Gr.

MISSISSIPPIAN
- Met — Etherington Fm.
- Mmh — Mount Head Fm.
- Mlv — Livingston Fm.
- Mbf — Exshaw and Banff Fms.
- Mbfu — Exshaw and Banff Fms. Upper part
- Mbfm — Exshaw and Banff Fms. Middle part
- Mbfl — Exshaw and Banff Fms. Lower part

DEVONIAN
- Dpa — Palliser Fm.
- Dax — Alexo Fm.
- Dsx — Southesk Fm.
- Dcn — Cairn Fm.

ORD.
- Oou — Outram Fm.

CAMB.-ORD.
- ЄOsp — Survey Peak Fm.

CAMBRIAN
- Єm — Mistaya Fm.
- Єbc — Bison Creek Fm.
- Єll — Lyell Fm.
- Єsu — Sullivan Fm.
- Єwf — Waterfowl Fm.
- Єar — Arctomys Fm.
- Єpk — Pika Fm.
- Єel — Eldon Fm.

Geological boundary (defined, approximate, assumed)

Bedding, tops known (horizontal, inclined, vertical, overturned)

Bedding, tops unknown (inclined)

Thrust fault (teeth on upthrust side)

Gravity fault (solid circle indicates downthrow side)

Other faults

Anticline (trace of axial surface)

Syncline (trace of axial surface)

Anticline, syncline (overturned)

Scale 1:50,000

0   1   2 miles

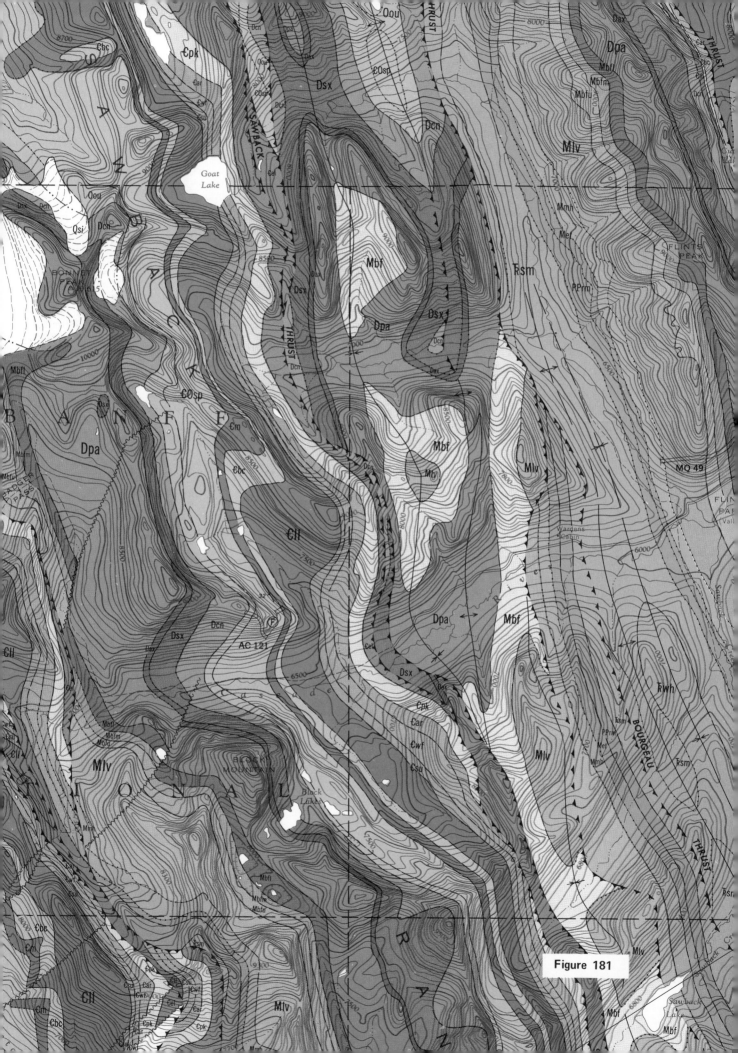

Figure 181

Geologic Map of the Central Pennsylvania Area

Figure 182 (p. 161). Central Pennsylvania

Problems

1. Identify the major anticlines and synclines and complete the geologic map by adding the proper symbols for fold axes. Show directions of plunge.

2. Identify the minor folds (both anticlines and synclines) in the central part of the map. How are the minor folds related to the major folds?

3. Study the large anticline shown in the northern part of the map. How could you identify this fold as an anticline if there were no explanation?

4. What was the orientation of the force that deformed this sequence of rocks?

5. Where are the oldest rocks exposed in the mapped area?

6. Draw an idealized north-south cross section across the map.

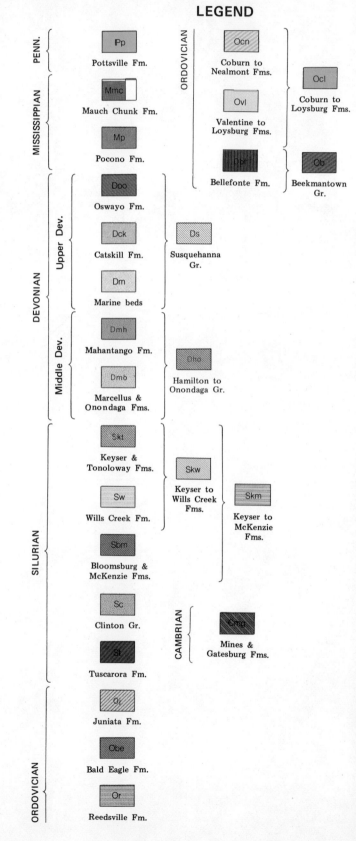

Scale 1:250,000

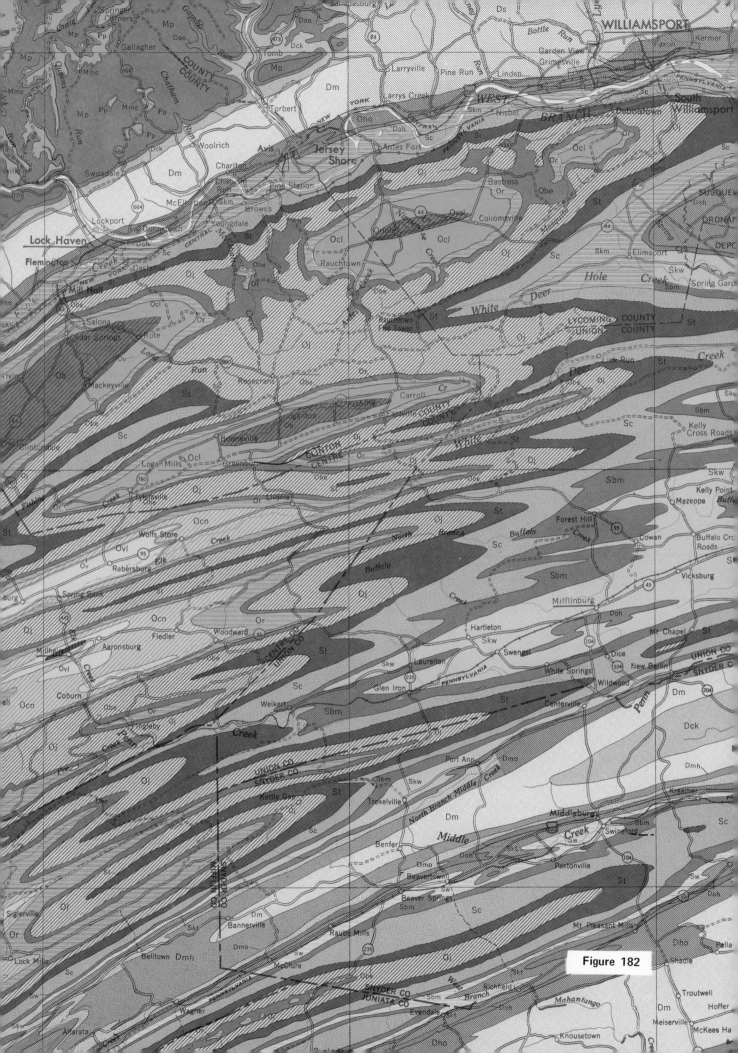

Figure 182

17 Tectonics of North America

Objective

To become acquainted with the major structural components of the North American continent and to understand how they fit into the theory of plate tectonics.

Main Concept

The major structural components of all continents are (1) the shield, (2) the stable platform, and (3) mobile mountain belts. These features can be explained by the theory of plate tectonics. According to this theory, continents grow by accretion and then split and drift apart as the plates move. Each continental fragment then becomes a center for further growth. Continents may also collide and be sutured together into a single large mass.

Supporting Ideas

1. The Canadian Shield is the oldest part of the North American continent. It consists of a series of semiconcentric belts of highly deformed metamorphic and igneous rocks. Each belt is thought to be the roots of an ancient mountain system that has been eroded to near sea level and is at isostatic equilibrium.
2. The stable platform is simply part of the shield that is covered with a thin veneer of horizontal or broadly warped Paleozoic or younger rocks.
3. Young, mobile mountain belts are located near the continental margins. They are believed to be the result of plate collision.
4. The spreading center of the oceanic ridge extends up the Gulf of California and can be projected northward, forming a rift system that is splitting part of North America away from the rest of the continent.

Discussion

The Shield

In North America the shield is exposed throughout most of eastern Canada, much of the Arctic Islands, and along the margins of parts of Greenland. It also apparently extends beneath the Greenland icecap (Figure 183). The southern and western margins of the shield are marked by a series of lakes, including the Great Lakes, Lake Winnipeg, Lake Athabaska, Great Slave Lake, and Great Bear Lake. The block diagram in Figure 183 will give you an idea of the structure of the shield. The rocks are highly deformed by compressive forces and have been injected by igneous intrusions, mostly granitic. The various belts of deformation in the shield have long been interpreted as the roots of ancient mountain systems. Exposures of metamorphic rocks which can form only at depths of several miles clearly indicate that erosion has removed a great amount of overlying rock to expose the metamorphic rocks that formed deep in the crust. Rocks of the shield are the oldest rocks found on the earth and range in age from 0.9 billion to 2.6 billion years.

The Stable Platform

Throughout a large part of the interior lowlands of North America, a thin veneer of Paleozoic and younger rocks covers the shield to form the stable platform (Figure 183). The stable platform includes the Great Plains to the west, the Interior Lowlands to the east, and the Coastal Plains. The sedimentary rocks are commonly warped into broad domes and basins, but the rocks are not tightly folded like those of a mountain belt.

Mountain Belts

The stable platform is flanked by two post-Cambrian mountain belts. The Appalachian Mountains to the east extend from New England to central Alabama and are characterized by tightly folded sedimentary rocks. Deformation occurred during late Paleozoic time (200 million years ago). The Cordillerian deformed belt to the west extends from Alaska to South America and was deformed by the collision of the westward-moving American plate with the Pacific plate during late Mesozoic and early Tertiary time (50 million to 70 million years ago).

Rift System

The oceanic rift system, which encircles the globe, can be traced across the eastern Pacific and up into the Gulf of California. The rift then extends northward into the western United States to produce the great block faulting of the Basin and Range in Nevada and western Utah. This part of the continent is under tensional stresses and ultimately fragments of the continent may split off.

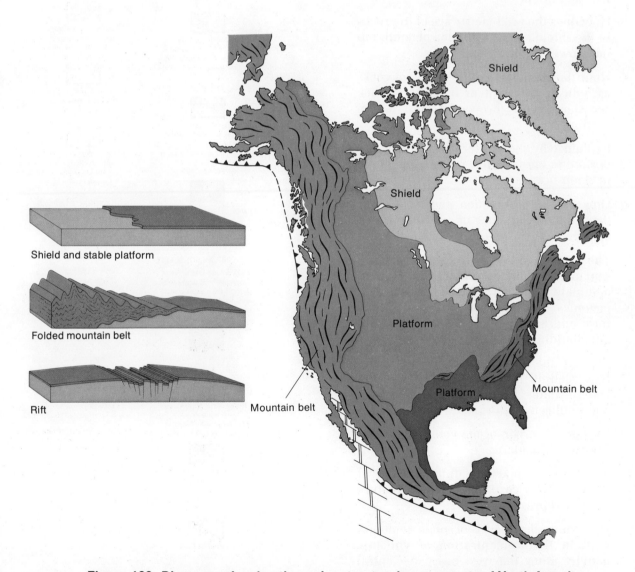

Figure 183. Diagrams showing the major structural components of North America.

Tectonic Features of North America

Figure 184 (p. 165). North America

Problems

1. Study the structural patterns of the shield. What evidence indicates that the shield consists of the roots of a series of deformed mountain belts? Indicate on the map by arrows the direction of compressive forces necessary to produce the structural trends in each major area of the shield.

2. If a mountain belt results from the collision of two lithospheric plates, how many major orogenic pulses are apparent in the exposed shield?

3. How does the radiometric age of the rocks in the shield support the idea of continental growth by accretion?

4. Note the thickness of the platform rocks as indicated by contour lines. How thick are these rocks throughout most of the platform?

5. Explain why the platform cover was deposited in very shallow water rather than in deep oceans.

6. How are the orientation and location of the mountain systems of North America explained by the theory of plate tectonics?

7. The bright red colors on the map represent granitic intrusions into young, folded mountain belts. Use the theory of plate tectonics to explain how the intrusions form and how they are related to mountain building (see p. 33).

8. Explain the origin of Baja, California. If spreading continues in the western United States, what will happen to Baja and southern California?

9. Explain the origin of the volcanoes in the Cascade Mountains.

10. Note the submarine contours west of Central America. What tectonic feature do they represent?

11. How does the theory of plate tectonics explain the concentration of volcanic activity along the west coast of Central America?

SEDIMENTARY UNITS

Thick deposits in structurally negative areas

Synorogenic and post-orogenic deposits

Miogesynclinal deposits

Eugeosynclinal desposits

Early geosynclinal deposits
Of Middle and Upper Proterozoic ages

Basement massifs
Mainly of Precambrian age. Includes metamorphic complexes that involve younger rocks

VOLCANIC AND PLUTONIC UNIT

Granitic plutons
Ages are generally within the span of the tectonic cycle of the foldbelts in which they lie

SPECIAL UNIT

Eugeosynclinal deposits of the Pacific border
Includes Franciscan Formation of California

PRECAMBRIAN FOLDBELTS

Dark colors show areas of paraschist and paragneiss derived from supracrustal rocks; light colors show areas of granite and orthogneiss of plutonic origin

Greenville foldbelt
Deformed 880-1,000 m.y. ago

Rocks of the Hudsonian foldbelt
Overprinted by Elsonian event about 1,370 m.y. ago

Hudsonian foldbelts
Deformed 1,640-1,820 m.y. ago

Kenoran foldbelts
Deformed 2,390-2,600 m.y. ago

Anorthosite bodies
In Greenville and Elsonian belts or, alternatively, in eastern Canadian Shield

PLATFORM AREAS

Ice cap of Quaternary age
On Precambrian and Paleozoic basement

Plateau basalts and associated rocks
In North Atlantic province

Platform deposits on Mesozoic basement
In Arctic Coastal Plain

Platform deposits on Paleozoic basement
In Atlantic and Gulf Coastal Plains

Platform deposits on Precambrian basement
In central-craton

Platform deposits within the Precambrian
Mainly in the Canadian Shield

STRUCTURAL SYMBOLS

Normal fault
Hachures on downthrown side

Transcurrent fault
Arrows show relative lateral movement

Thrust fault
Barbs on upthrown side

Subsea fault
Long dashes based on topographic and geophysical evidence; short dashes, based on geophysical evidence only

Axes of sea-floor spreading

Flexure
Arrows on depressed side

Salt domes and salt diapirs
In Gulf Coastal Plain and Gulf of Mexico

Volcano

+2000
0
2000

Contours on basement surfaces beneath platform areas
All contours are below sea level except where marked with plus symbols. Interval 2,000 meters

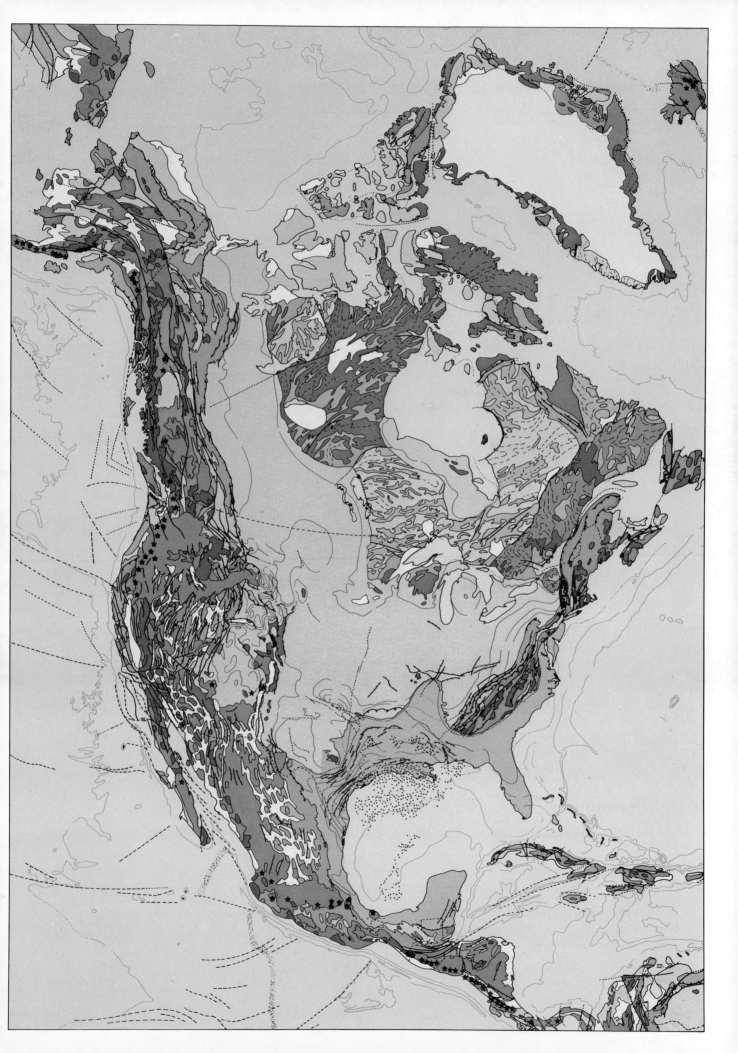

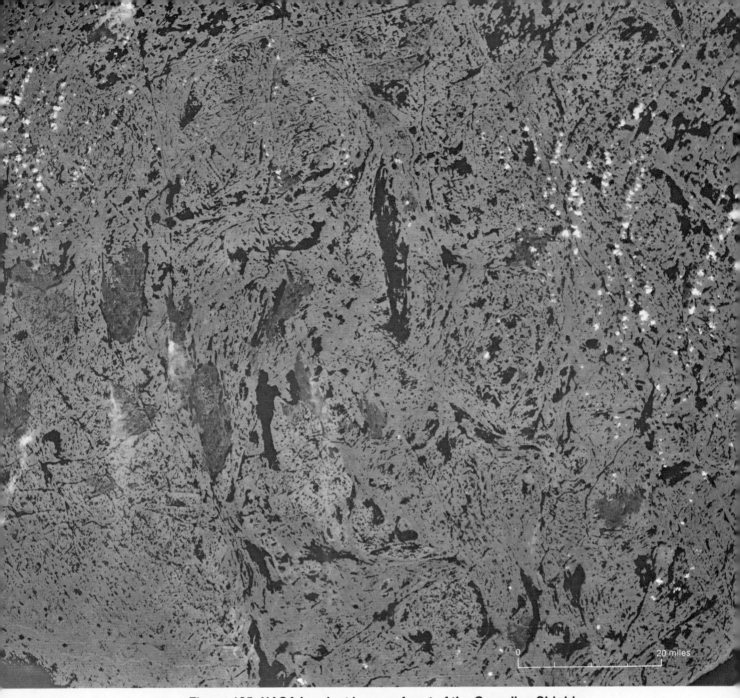

Figure 185. NASA Landsat image of part of the Canadian Shield.

Figure 185 shows an area north of Great Slave Lake in northwestern Canada. Metamorphic rocks appear in tones of reddish brown; granitic rocks are dark greenish gray. Differences in local relief are generally only 200 to 300 feet.

Problems

1. What is the general shape of the granitic bodies? What type of igneous intrusions are they?

2. Study the structural trends of the metamorphic rocks, which are commonly expressed by linear lakes. What evidence can you find that these rocks have been intensely deformed by horizontal stresses in the crust?

3. Why would you conclude that the rocks in the shield are roots of ancient mountains?

4. Why would you conclude that great volumes of rock have been eroded from the shield?

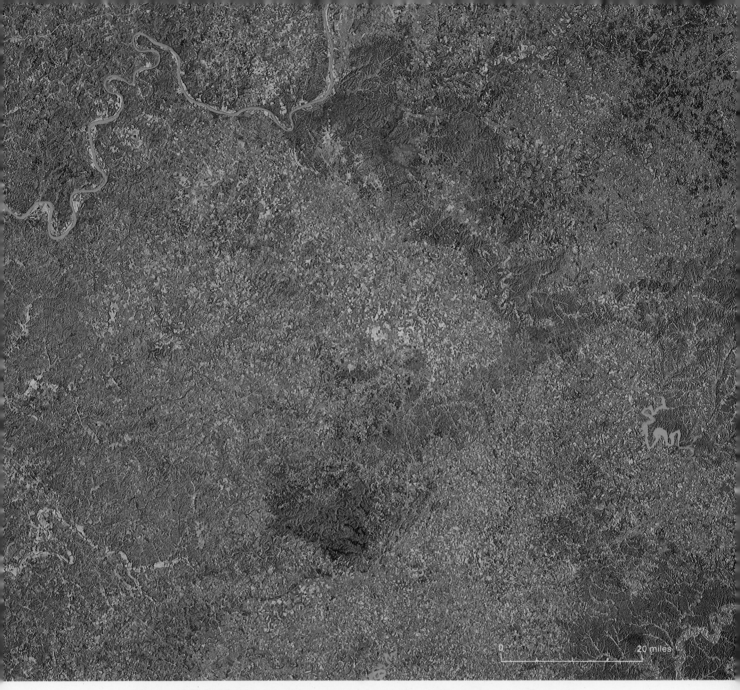

Figure 186. NASA Landsat image of part of the stable platform—Kentucky.

This Landsat image shows part of the central interior lowlands of the United States, an area of the stable platform where the horizontal rocks are undisturbed.

Problems

1. How does the deformation of the stable platform differ from that of mountain belts?

2. Compare the shield and the stable platform (Figures 185 and 186). What is the major difference between them?

3. Why are the rocks of the stable platform predominantly shallow marine sediments?

167

Figure 187. NASA Landsat image of a folded mountain belt—Appalachian Mountains, Pennsylvania.

The entire sequence of sedimentary rocks in this area (nearly 40,000 feet thick) has been deformed into a series of tight folds. The resistant formations have been eroded into prominent ridges which zigzag across the landscape. The low, intervening valleys are eroded on nonresistant shale and limestone formations.

Problems

1. Select a prominent ridge and trace its extent across the area. Refer to the map patterns of plunging folds (p. 144) and label the anticlines and synclines.

2. Draw an idealized cross section across the folded belt to show the style and degree of deformation. Show the folds below the surface with solid lines and show the parts of the folds that have been eroded away (above the surface) with dashed lines.

3. Show by arrows the direction of the stresses that produced this deformation.

Figure 188. NASA Landsat image of the Basin and Range—Lovelock, Nevada.

The geology of the Basin and Range is complex, but in general the basins are downdropped blocks of the crust that result from tensional stress in the crust. The basins are partly filled with sediment derived from the adjacent ranges.

Problems

1. Draw an idealized cross section of this area, showing the style and degree of deformation.

2. What geologic and geophysical phenomena would you expect to occur in this area?

3. What will this area likely evolve into if the tectonic forces continue?

18 Geology of the Ocean Floor

Objectives

To become familiar with the geology of the ocean floor and to understand how the major structural and topographic features of the ocean floor fit into the theory of plate tectonics.

Main Concept

The topography of the ocean floor has been mapped by means of seismic reflection profiles. The profiles indicate the topographic form and shallow structure of features on the ocean floor. The major features of the ocean floor are (1) the oceanic ridge, (2) the abyssal floor, (3) fracture zones, (4) seamounts, (5) deep-sea trenches, and (6) continental margins.

Supporting Ideas

1. The oceanic ridge is a broad, fractured swell, or arch. Sediment is thin or absent on the crest and thickest on the flanks of the ridge.
2. The abyssal floor consists of abyssal hills and abyssal plains.
3. Fracture zones cut the oceanic ridge and show strong evidence of strike-slip movement and horizontal displacement of the sea floor.
4. The size, shape, composition, and structure of seamounts indicate that they are submarine shield volcanoes.
5. Deep-sea trenches are long, linear depressions of the sea floor adjacent to the most active seismic and volcanic zones in the world.
6. The continental slopes are the margins of the continents. They are cut by numerous submarine canyons.

Discussion

One of the most significant advances in our understanding of the earth—the revolutionary concept of sea-floor spreading and plate tectonics—has been made possible by new techniques for mapping the sea floor. The seismic profiler is an especially effective instrument because it makes a continuous profile of the sea floor as the ship moves and it also makes a profile of the layers of sediment and rock beneath the sea floor. By means of low-frequency sound waves the seismic profiler detects the interfaces of rock layers as well as the interface of sea floor and sea water. These data are plotted automatically as the ship moves, creating a topographic and structural profile of the ocean floor. The information obtained from thousands of seismic profiles has been used to map the relief of the sea floor with an accuracy comparable to that of preliminary topographic maps of the land. Maps and charts compiled from recent oceanographic studies show that the sea floor has many unique, spectacular features.

Seismic Profiles

Figure 189. Seismic profile of the east flank of the mid-Atlantic Ridge.

Problems

1. The sediment accumulating in the open ocean is derived largely from the shells of floating organisms. Explain why the sediment is much thicker on the flanks of the mid-Atlantic Ridge than near the crest.

2. The mid-Atlantic Ridge is commonly described as a broad arch or swell that has been broken by faults. Draw all the major faults on the profile.

3. What evidence is there that this segment of the crust is under tension rather than compression?

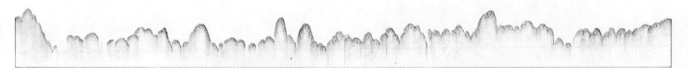

Figure 190. Seismic profile of abyssal hills in the Pacific.

Problems

1. Briefly describe the topography of the abyssal hills. (Consider their shape, size, and distribution.)

2. Abyssal hills are probably the most widespread topographic feature of our planet. What is their origin?

Figure 191. Seismic profile of fracture zones.

Problems

1. The profile above is taken across the trend of the fracture zone and shows many features perpendicular to this structure. What evidence is there that the "fractures" are faults?

2. Draw the faults on the profile. Do they occur along a single fracture or along a fracture zone?

3. Maps of the ocean floor show great horizontal displacement along the fracture. Is there apparent vertical displacement as well? Explain.

Figure 192. Seismic profile of abyssal plains west of Africa. The scale of this profile is much larger than that of the abyssal hills, and considerably more detail is shown.

Problems

1. What is the major difference between abyssal hills and abyssal plains?

2. How do abyssal plains originate?

3. Why do geologists assume that the oceanic crust has not been subjected to strong compressive forces and is therefore fundamentally different from continental crusts?

4. What type of deformation has taken place in the sediments near the right side of the profile?

5. Note the asymmetry of the large, partly buried hill in the left part of the profile. Is there evidence of tension in the part of the oceanic crust that is older than the sediment?

Figure 193. Seismic profile of deep-sea trenches—Vitvaz and north New Hebrides.

Problems

1. Is there evidence of sediment (a) in the trench and (b) in the areas adjacent to the trench?

2. How would you explain the distribution (presence or absence) of sediment on this part of the ocean floor?

3. Note the difference in the height on either side of the trench. Explain this difference in light of the plate tectonics theory.

4. What evidence of faulting can you find on the walls of the trench? Draw the probable faults on the profile and explain how they may have originated.

Figure 194. Seismic profile of seamounts between Hawaii and Japan.

Problems

1. What evidence do you see in the profile that seamounts are volcanic in origin?

2. What type of volcano forms the seamounts?

3. What evidence is there that faulting and sedimentation occur on the seamounts?

4. What type of sea-floor topography occurs adjacent to the seamounts?

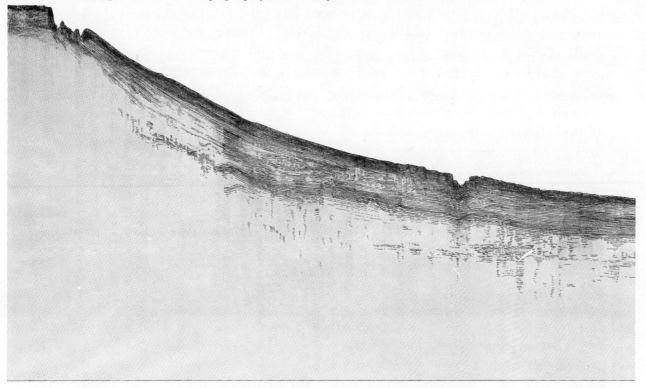

Figure 195. Seismic profile of continental slope.

Problems

1. What are the "channels" cut into the surface of the continental slope?

2. How does the rock which makes up the slope compare with the rock of (a) abyssal plains, (b) abyssal hills, (c) seamounts, and (d) the flanks of the mid-Atlantic Ridge?

3. What is the source of sediment on the continental slope? Has the sediment on the continental slope been deformed? Cite evidence to support your answer.

4. What geologic process is, and has been, active on the continental slope—folding, faulting, sedimentation, or erosion?

Major Topographic and Structural Features
of the Ocean Floor

Figure 196 (p. 175). Atlantic Ocean

The physiographic maps on pages 175 and 177 represent, in perspective, the regional features that have been mapped on the ocean floor. Although there is considerable vertical exaggeration and generalization, the essential elements of the maps are firmly established.

Problems

1. What topographic evidence is there that the continental crust is different from the oceanic crust?

2. Note the numerous canyons carved on the continental slopes. What is their probable origin?

3. Why are there no abyssal hills adjacent to the continental slope?

4. Study the fracture system of the mid-Atlantic Ridge. How do these features support the theory of plate tectonics?

5. Study the physiography of the ocean floor. Where would you expect the greatest number of earthquakes to occur? How does this support the theory of plate tectonics?

6. Color the rift valley at the crest of the mid-Atlantic Ridge red. What types of stresses are implied by the way the ridge has been displaced along the fracture zone?

7. If you were to test the theory of plate tectonics by deep-sea drilling and geophysical studies, where would you plan a drilling program to find

    a. the oldest sediments of the sea floor?

    b. the thickest sediments of the sea floor?

    c. the youngest rocks of the sea floor?

    d. the area of greatest seismic activity?

    e. the area of maximum heat flow?

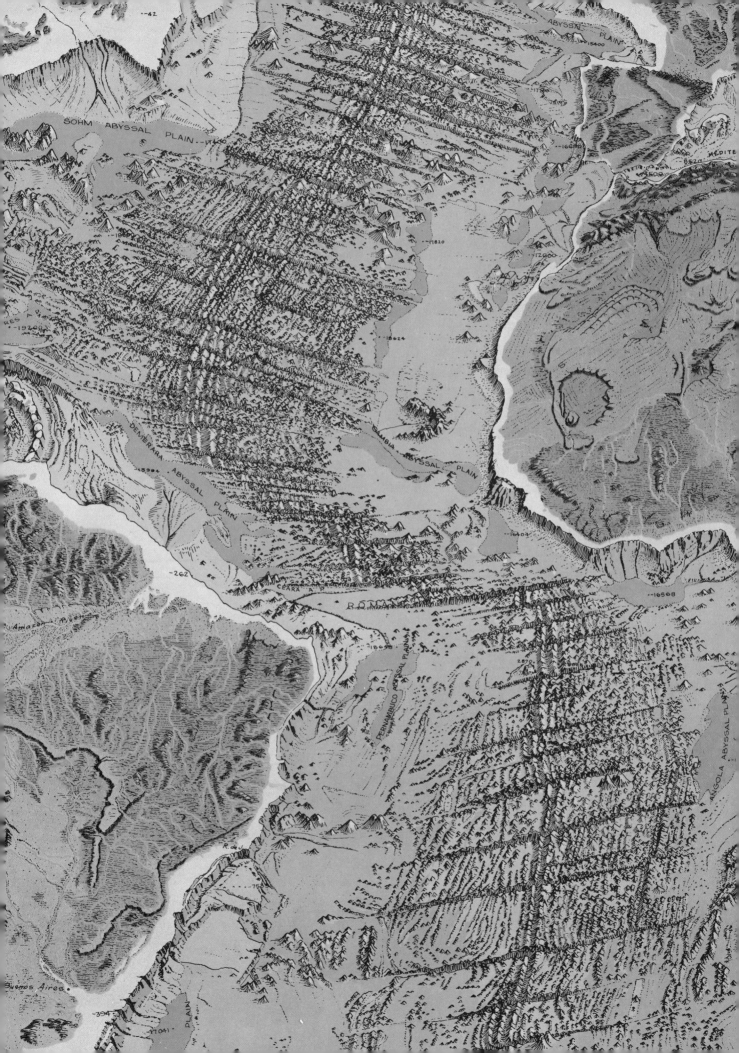

Major Topographic and Structural Features
of the Ocean Floor

Figure 197 (p. 177). Pacific Ocean

Problems

1. Sketch the trend of the deep-sea trenches. How are the trenches related to island arcs? How are trenches and island arcs explained by the theory of plate tectonics?

2. Note the linear trends of many of the seamounts. If the theory that these volcanoes developed from the lithospheric plate passing over a "hot spot" is correct, where would you expect to find the oldest island or seamount?

3. Many of the seamounts have flat tops. If the plates are moving, how would you expect the flat surfaces of seamounts to be tilted as they approach the trench?

4. The sediment covering the abyssal plain is largely derived from the adjacent continents. Why are there only a few abyssal plains in the margins of the Pacific?

5. Recent drilling in the northwest Pacific has uncovered deposits of shells of organisms that thrive only in warm water near the equator. How would you explain this anomaly by the theory of plate tectonics?

6. Explain why Japan has numerous severe earthquakes but central Australia has very few.

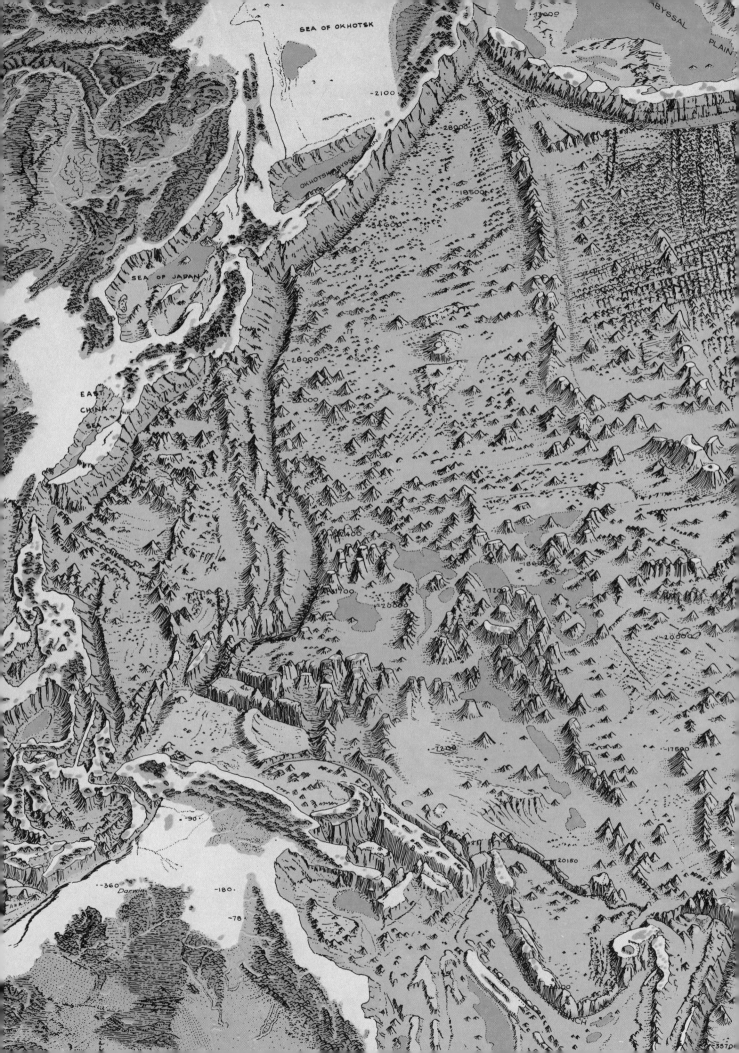

SEA OF OKHOTSK

ABYSSAL

PLAIN

-2100

-28000

OKHOTSK ABYSSAL PLAIN

-18500

-34600

-28000

-22000

-20400

-1860

-11000

-1720

-20000

-20000

-7200

-17500

-90

-20150

-360 Darwin

-180

-78

-357.00

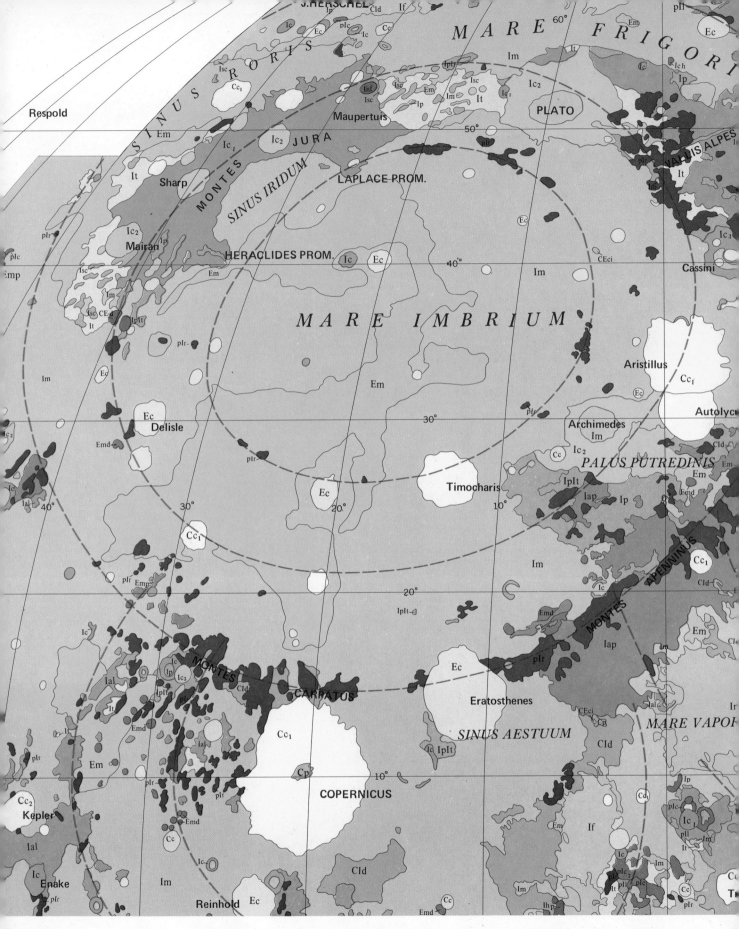

Figure 198. Geologic map of the Mare Imbrium area of the moon.

0   800 miles

19 **Planetary Geology**

Objective

To recognize the major landforms of the planetary bodies of the solar system and to understand the processes that formed them. To use this information to compare the earth's geology with the geology of other planetary bodies and thereby recognize which processes are fundamental to all and which are unique or of special importance.

Main Concept

The rocks and surface features of the moon, Mercury, and Mars contain a record of events which occurred early in the evolutionary development of the planets. Those events were largely the result of impact during a period of intense bombardment, followed by floods of basaltic lava. None of the planets explored to date shows evidence of plate tectonics similar to that on the earth.

Supporting Ideas

1. The impact of meteorites produces a crater and a new rock body consisting mostly of breccia thrown out to form a blanket of ejecta which surrounds the crater.
2. The sequence of events in the geologic history of each planet can be determined by using the principle of superposition.
3. The moon and Mercury are strikingly similar in size, surface features, and geologic history. Both are primitive bodies dominated by impact structures, and their surfaces have not undergone significant changes from either atmospheric erosion or internal tectonism.
4. Mars has had a much more complex history than the moon. Its surface has been modified by running water, wind, volcanic activity, and tectonic forces. The style of tectonism suggests that Mars represents a phase of planetary development between that of primitive, impact-dominated bodies, such as the moon and Mercury, and that of tectonically active Earth.
5. The Galilean moons of Jupiter are totally different from the terrestrial planets in both composition and place of origin. The surface of each moon is unique and records different processes and sequences of events.

Discussion

Most scientists believe that the planets were formed by the accretion of matter from a cold, dry, dusty cloud of gas which had some degree of internal motion. The small particles collected by gravitational attraction into increasingly larger, solid bodies called planetoids, which were up to several miles in diameter. Accretion of the planetoids by gravitational attraction eventually formed a planet, which swept up most of the planetoids and meteorites in its orbital path.

The dominant surface features of the moon, Mercury, and Mars are impact craters probably resulting from the last phases of accretion. The impact process, in simple terms, produces two geologic features: (1) an impact crater and (2) a body of fragmented rock thrown out of the crater by impact (an *ejecta blanket*), with smaller particles thrown out great distances to form huge splash marks called *rays*.

On the basis of superposition of ejecta and/or volcanic material, the relative sequence of many events on the moon, Mercury, and Mars can be determined. The moons of Jupiter are unique in composition and surface features, but their history can be interpreted according to the same principles used in studying the terrestrial planets.

Geology of the Moon, Mercury, and Mars

Figure 199 (p. 181). Photo of the Mare Imbrium area of the moon

Compare the photo of the Imbrium Basin with the geologic map (Figure 198, p. 178).

Problems

1. What evidence is there in the photograph that Archimedes, Plato, and their ejecta blankets (shown in light blue) are older than Aristillus, Autolycus, and Timocharis (shown in yellow) and Eratosthenes (shown in green)?

2. Note that the Imbrium Basin is considered to be a multiringed crater. What evidence for this is shown on the photograph?

3. What photographic evidence can you find that the crater Sinus Iridum and its ejecta blanket (shown in dark blue) are younger than the ejecta of the multiringed crater which forms the Imbrium Basin?

4. What photographic evidence shows that Copernicus and its ejecta blanket are the youngest features in the area?

5. Arrange the following moon features in their proper chronological sequence:

   a. Eratosthenes (ejecta blanket)

   b. Mare Imbrium (basalt flows)

   c. Archimedes (ejecta)

   d. Copernicus (ejecta)

   e. Sinus Iridum (ejecta)

Figure 200. Orbiting satellite photo of the eastern part of the Imbrium Basin.

Problems

1. Explain the difference in the morphology of the three largest craters and their associated ejecta blankets.

2. Study the three large craters in this area and determine their relative ages.

3. Where are the oldest rocks? What event in lunar history do they represent?

4. Where are the youngest rocks?

Figure 201. Photomosaic of Mercury.

Problems

1. Study the large circular basin near the twilight zone and compare it with the Imbrium Basin in the moon. What is the origin of this feature?

2. Note that many of the craters in the left central part of the photo (including the large basin) have a flat floor and appear to be covered or obscured with a smooth plains-forming material. What is the most probable origin of this material?

3. What are the youngest features on Mercury?

4. What are the oldest features on Mercury?

5. Compare and contrast the surface features and general geologic history of the moon and Mercury.

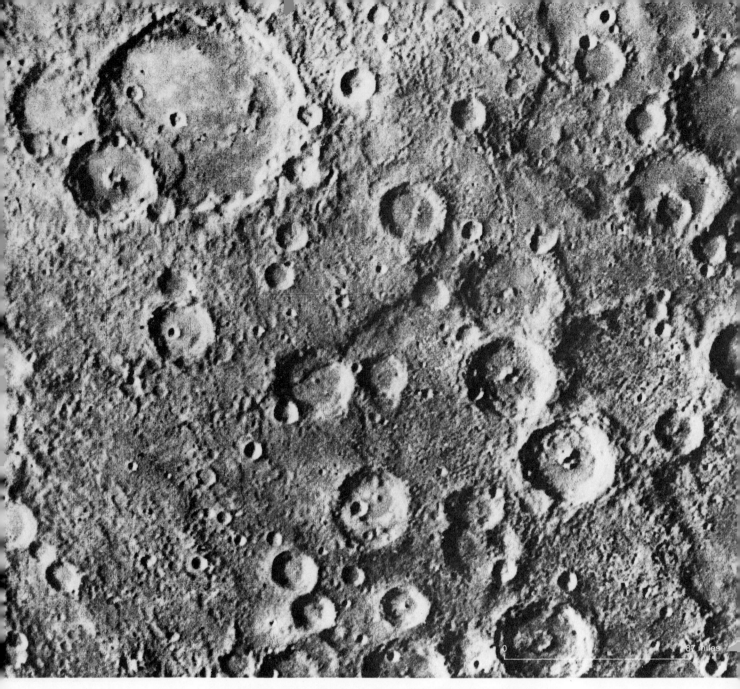

Figure 202. Densely cratered terrain of Mercury.

Problems

1. Make a generalized sketch map of the surface features in the northwest quarter of this area and determine the relative ages of the largest craters.

2. Study the cliff which makes a broad arc from the upper right to the center of the photo. What process formed this feature?

3. Is the medium-sized crater in the center of the photo older or younger than the scarp? Defend your answer.

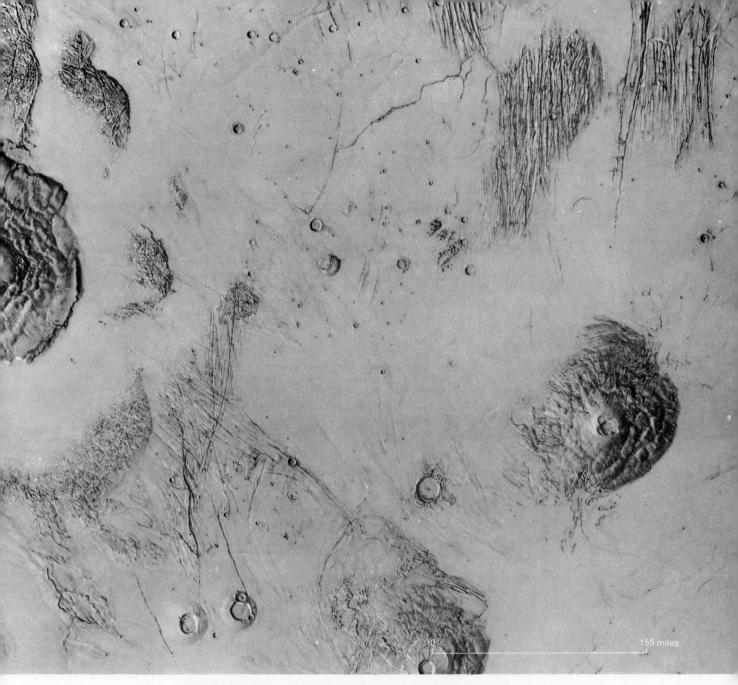

Figure 203. Physiographic map of the Tharsis area, Mars.

Problems

1. What is the diameter of the volcano Olympus Mons? How does this compare with the shield volcanoes which form the island of Hawaii (125 miles in diameter)?

2. Is there any evidence that Olympus Mons has been modified by erosion?

3. What is the origin of the channels radiating from the summit of the three large volcanoes in this area?

4. There are several types of geologic features in this area: volcanoes, faults, ejecta from craters, and smooth plains material (presumably maria basalt and windblown dust). Arrange them in chronological order.

5. What type of lava would form (a) the smooth plains and (b) the large volcanoes?

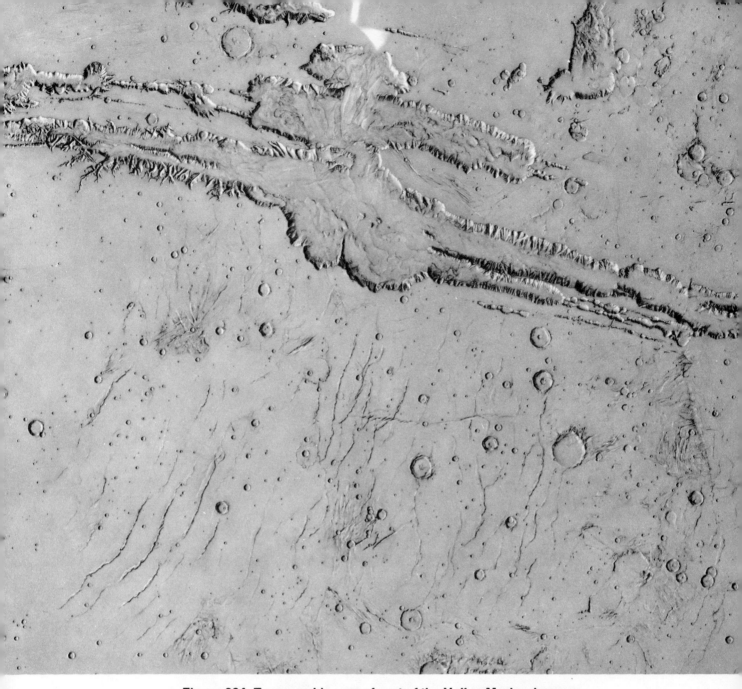

Figure 204. Topographic map of part of the Valles Marinaris area.

Problems

1. The great Valles Marinaris is one of the major landforms on Mars. It extends across this entire map and beyond, a distance of nearly 2000 miles. Study the shape of this canyon. What evidence is there that it was formed by erosion? What evidence is there that it was formed by rifting (faulting) of the crust?

2. Study the walls of the canyon, especially in the western part. How have the walls been modified?

3. How does the Valles Marinaris differ from the great canyons on the earth? What does this suggest concerning its origin?

4. Which of the following features on the earth do you consider most similar to the Valles Marinaris: (a) the Grand Canyon of the Colorado River, (b) the Red Sea rift, (c) submarine canyons, (d) the Atlantic Ocean basin, or (e) the Basin and Range of the western United States?

186

The Moons of Jupiter

The four large moons of Jupiter were discovered by Galileo in 1610 and are often referred to as the Galilean satellites. Until recently they were known only as tiny specks of light in a telescopic field of view, but in March and July of 1979 the Voyager spacecrafts sent back thousands of photographs of these satellites and unmasked four new worlds for geologic exploration. The Voyager pictures show that the Galilean moons not only are complex, but each appears to be unique, with surface features that vary greatly in age, composition, appearance, and geologic history. It seems clear that the new data will be the basis for an exciting new understanding of the Jupiter system, and studies of comparative planetology will provide new insight into our own planet.

The Galilean satellites are shown in Figures 205 through 208. They were formed in an environment totally different from that of the terrestrial planets. In the outer solar system it is much colder and there are greater quantities of volatile material (denser material is concentrated near the inner solar system and formed the dense, rocky terrestrial planets). These environmental differences caused differences in the composition and evolution of the planetary bodies.

Callisto is the outermost and darkest Galilean moon. It is approximately 50 percent water ice, which forms a thick mantle surrounding a relatively small "rocky" core. Dust and debris from space cover and dirty the surface of Callisto, but clean white ice from below the surface is commonly "splashed out" by the impact of meteorites.

Ganymede is also approximately 50 percent ice. Together with Callisto it represents a class of low-density planetary bodies that has never before been studied in detail. Both planets are much lighter than any rock (they are not even twice as dense as water). Dark areas on Ganymede are probably dirty ice and light areas relatively clean ice.

Europa is made up mostly of silicate rock material (note the densities given in Table 7), with water ice forming a relatively thin outer shell, possibly as thick as 200 miles. In a sense Europa is covered with a global ocean of frozen ice, possibly with liquid water or slushy ice below a frozen crust.

Io, the innermost Galilean satellite, is unlike any other object in the solar system. Eight erupting volcanoes were observed during the brief encounter of Voyager 1, and six were seen to be still active four months later by Voyager 2. Io is the most volcanically active body in the solar system, so it is not surprising that its surface is dominated by a variety of volcanic features including large caldera, lava flows, volcanic plains, and probably volcanic phenomena not observed on earth. Sulfur is the main element ejected by the volcanoes of Io. It is spewed out as liquid flows, particles from lava foundations, and "ash." Sulfur can occur in an amazing variety of colors, including red, orange, brown, yellow, white, and black. It is believed that the vivid red-orange color of Io is due largely to sulfur.

TABLE 7. JUPITER'S MOONS

Satellite	Radius (km)	Density (g/cm^3)	Surface Material
Io	1820	3.57	Sulfur compound
Europa	1565	3.40	Ice
Ganymede	2641	1.93	Ice
Callisto	2420	1.83	Ice

Problems

In answering the questions that follow, remember that the age of a planetary surface is reflected by the relative number of impact structures. Old surfaces have been subjected to long periods of bombardment and are saturated with craters. Younger surfaces have fewer craters.

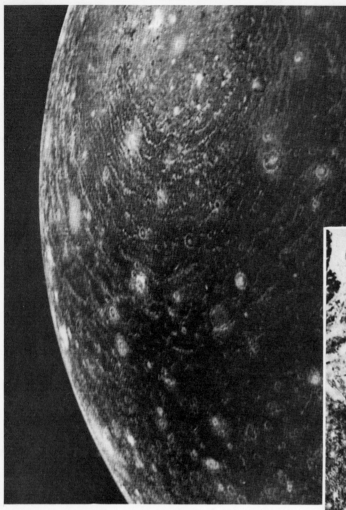

Figure 205. Callisto.

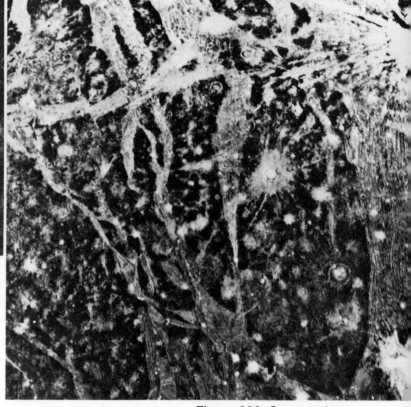

Figure 206. Ganymede.

Callisto

1. What landform dominates the surface of Callisto?

2. What is the probable origin of the large multiringed structure?

3. How does the geologic history of Callisto compare with that of the moon and Mercury?

Ganymede

1. Judging from the relative number of craters, which terrain type is older, the dark fragmented terrain or the light grooved terrain?

2. What are the youngest features on Ganymede?

3. What evidence is there that the crust of Ganymede has moved and shifted horizontally?

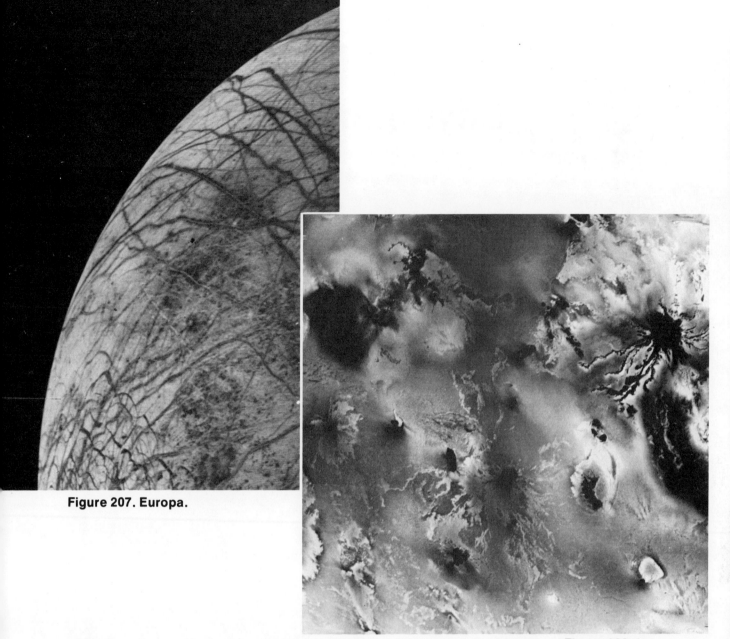

Figure 207. Europa.

Figure 208. Io.

Europa

1. What is the probable origin of the linear structure on Europa?

2. Is the surface of Europa older, younger, or about the same age as that of Callisto? Cite evidence to defend your answer.

3. Compare and contrast the surface of Europa with that of Ganymede. Could the surface of Europa represent the initial stages in the development of the type of terrain on Ganymede?

Io

1. On the photograph of Io identify and label the following features: (a) major centers of volcanic eruption, (b) lava flows, (c) plains covered with sulfur and salts, and (d) active volcanic eruptions.

2. Why do geologists believe that the surface of Io is much younger than the surfaces of the other Galilean moons?

3. What is the origin of the volcanic activity on Io?

20 Environmental Geology

Objective

To understand the relationship between geologic systems and the environment.

Main Concept

The surface of the earth, the environment in which we live, is in delicate balance with the geologic processes that produce it. Our modification of those processes may upset the balance and significantly alter the environment, with many unforeseen side effects. A careful study of geologic and topographic maps and aerial photographs will usually reveal the geologic processes operating in a particular region and the major problems that might be encountered in that region.

Supporting Ideas

Some of the major problems in environmental geology include the following:

I. Geologic hazards
    A. Movement of crustal materials
        1. Faulting
        2. Vulcanism
        3. Isostatic adjustment
    B. Movement of surface materials
        1. Mass movement along slopes
        2. Surface subsidence (may result from removal of ores, oil, and ground water)
    C. Movement of earth materials
        1. Stream systems
        2. Shoreline systems
        3. Eolian systems
        4. Glacier systems
II. Environmental alterations
    A. Changes in land contours
        1. Strip-mining
        2. Construction (urban and highway)
    B. Disruption of drainage systems (e.g., dam construction)
    C. Changes in ground-water table (e.g., irrigation)
    D. Modification of current and wave action (e.g., coastal installations)
    E. Pollution from waste disposal
        1. Gaseous wastes (atmosphere)
        2. Liquid wastes (ground-water aquifers, drainage systems, lakes, oceans)
        3. Solid wastes (land surface)
        4. Radioactive wastes (atmosphere, water, land)
    F. Modification from recreation

Figure 209. San Francisco, California, 1956.

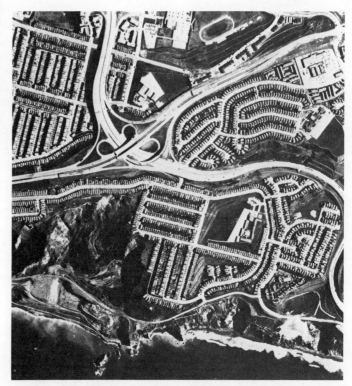

Figure 210. San Francisco, California, 1971.

Geologic Hazards in San Francisco, California

Potential geologic hazards include (1) the San Andreas fault, (2) landslide areas, (3) stream erosion, and (4) shoreline retreat.

Problems

1. What physical changes occurred during the 15-year period shown? How will these changes proceed in the future?

2. Assuming urban expansion in the area was inevitable, what areas should have been developed and what areas left in a natural state?

3. What special hazards exist for the two schools and playground areas?

4. In the event of some minor movement along the San Andreas fault, what damage can be expected?

Environmental Problems in South Dade County, Florida

Figure 211 (p. 193). South Dade County

At every place on the earth's surface there exists some real or potential environmental hazard. An excellent example is south Dade County, Florida, adjacent to Miami. In recent years the rapid urban development in this area has become a serious threat to the environment, despite the efforts of Dade County residents to maintain environmental quality.

Most of the land surface in south Dade County is less than 10 feet above high-tide level, and the highest areas are only 25 feet above sea level.

Water is the primary environmental concern of south Dade County. For this reason Dade and adjacent counties are part of a regional water control system developed to conserve and protect surface and ground water and to control fresh- and salt-water flooding. It includes management of the drainage canals as well as conservation and storage areas.

The major drainageways, shown on the topographic map (Figure 211), are man-made canals or modifications of existing drainageways. They form a system to reduce flood damage from storm and tide and to conserve fresh water. A limestone sequence underlying the area contains two aquifers. The upper one, the Biscayne Aquifer, extends from the surface to as much as 120 feet below ground and is the source of fresh water for the area. The other aquifer, the Floridian Aquifer, is more than 800 feet below the surface and contains only brackish and salt water.

Water problems now being faced by south Dade County are saltwater intrusion into the Biscayne Aquifer, contamination of the aquifer by recharge from canal and surface waters, and depletion of water from the aquifer. Demand for water to serve the residents of the community lowers the water table in the Everglades and threatens the natural flora and fauna there.

In an area of such low-lying topography there are serious drainage problems. Flooding is always a potential hazard. Drainage canals have helped control flooding, but unfortunately the canals adversely affect the ecosystem of the Everglades by diverting the swamp's source of fresh water. To prevent drainage problems in urban areas, building codes requiring a minimum elevation for lots and streets have been established. Storm runoff increases flooding from high tides caused by hurricanes.

South Dade County faces the environmental problems that plague all urban areas, plus problems created by the county's particular physical characteristics. Changes are rapid as the natural forests and the Everglades are converted to agricultural use and, eventually, to commercial and residential development.

Problems

1. What areas would be most susceptible to damage from hurricanes and heavy rainfall?

2. What effect would the keys have on hurricanes approaching from offshore?

3. What particular problems need to be considered in building on a limestone terrain?

4. Why has most of the urbanization of this area been concentrated in its present location?

5. How would you expect the patterns of urbanization to appear 20 years hence?

6. What would be the best sites for the disposal of solid waste? Why?

7. What problems are likely to result from excessive pumping of ground water?

Florida

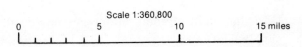

Scale 1:360,800

0   5   10   15 miles

Figure 212. Santa Clara County, California, 1948.

Hydrology and Urbanization

The accompanying aerial photos show part of Santa Clara County, California, before and after extensive urbanization. Between 1948 and 1968 the impermeable area increased dramatically. An urban area was developed on alluvial fans at the base of the Santa Cruz Mountains. Most of the rainfall in this area occurs as brief storms from November through March.

Problems

1. On the two air photos trace the drainageways before and after urbanization. Do the patterns differ?

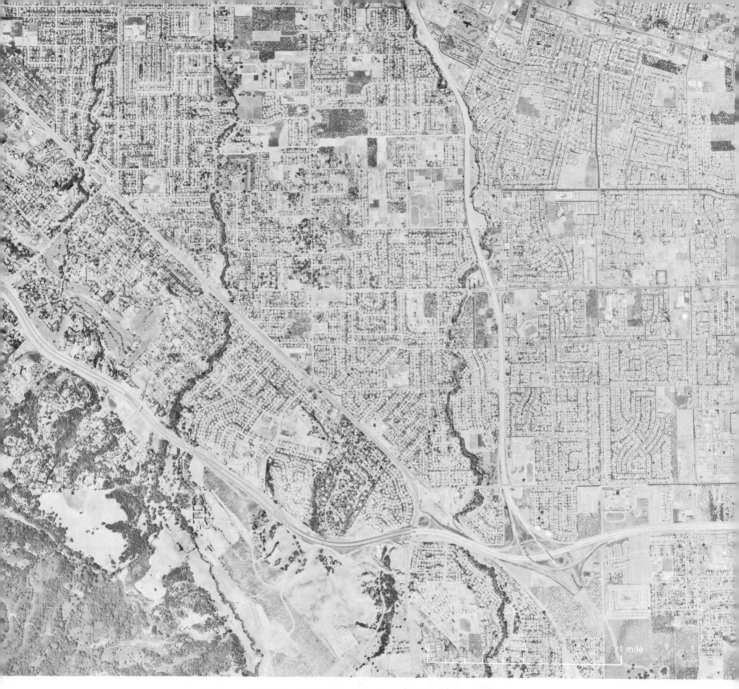

Figure 213. Santa Clara County, California, 1968.

2. Estimate the increase in the percentage of impermeable area due to urbanization.

3. In light of your answers to problems 1 and 2, what effects would urbanization in this area have on storm runoff? What effect would urban development have outside this area?

4. Since urban growth is inevitable, what are some possible solutions to these problems?

5. What effect does increased urbanization have on ground-water recharge?

6. Flash floods are common in this part of the country. Locate areas where this hazard is likely to be most serious.

195

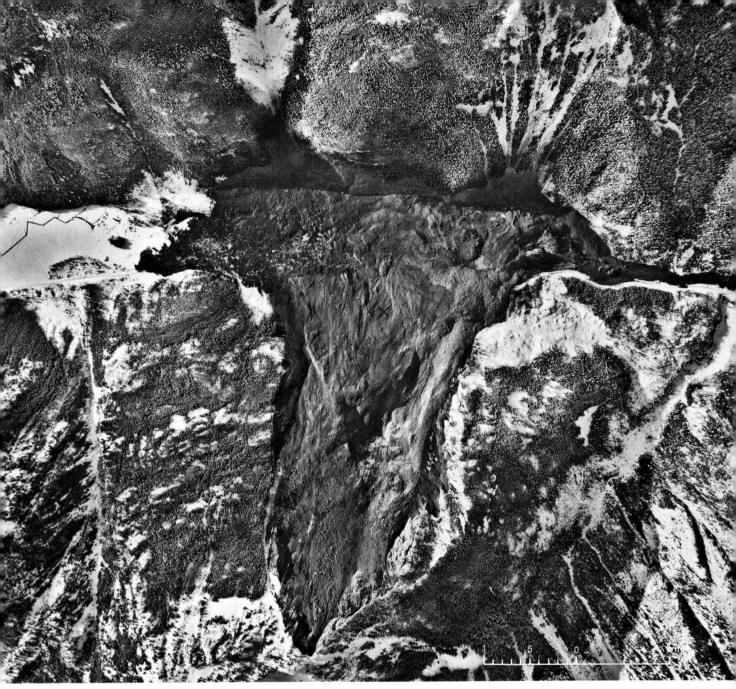

Figure 214. British Columbia, Canada.

Mass Movement

Problems

1. What types of mass movement have occurred in this area?

2. What natural geologic conditions exist which would be conducive to mass movement?

3. The major problem caused by landslides has been the disruption of the transportation system through the main canyon. How will transportation be restored, and how can people cope with such hazards in the future?

4. What other locations in this area are likely sites of mass movement? Where has mass movement occurred in the past?

21 Supplementary Exercises with Stereo Photographs

Aerial photographs are invaluable aids to geologic study. They are used extensively for map interpretation and mineral exploration. The great value of aerial photographs is that they provide an extraordinarily accurate and detailed model of the earth's surface. It is quite easy to recognize such familiar features as roads, buildings, and lakes, and with a little experience various types of terrain and rock bodies can be identified too. Aerial photographs are thus exceptionally useful for studying landforms and surface processes. In fact, many features are revealed better by photographs than by studies done on the ground.

Although single prints are suitable for preliminary observations, more data can be obtained from stereo photographs, and so it is very important that you learn to use the stereoscope effectively. The following instructions will help:

1. Orient the stereo pairs in the proper relative positions, the left print on the left and the right print on the right.
2. The center point of each photo in a pair is marked with a +. A line on the photographs connecting the center points is the *base line*. This line should be parallel to the eye base (an imaginary line between the pupils of your eyes) when you are looking through the stereoscope.
3. Place the photos under the stereoscope in the proper relative positions, so that the surface details on one photograph can be matched with corresponding details on the other.
4. As you look through the stereoscope, move the photographs parallel to the base line until the center points appear to be superimposed. (To get the best possible stereo model, you must always separate the photos in the direction of the flight line.) You should now have stereo vision. If you don't, rotate the photographs slightly.
5. Once you have achieved stereo vision, you may preserve the alignment by attaching the photos to the desk top with a small piece of masking tape.

Stereo vision comes easily for some people, but others encounter difficulties. If you have trouble, try locating a feature common to both photos and marking it with a dot or a circle. Then you can concentrate on these common points while you shift the photographs parallel to the base line until the marks are superimposed. Another helpful technique is to place the index finger of each hand on a point common to each photo and then shift the photos until the points of your fingers appear to be superimposed.

Stereoscopic relief can be obtained only for overlap area. With a lens stereoscope, the width of the field of view is only about 2 inches. If the position of overlap is reversed, however, nearly all of the overlap area can be viewed in stereo (see Figure 215). You can also increase the area in stereo view by slightly lifting and bending the top photograph.

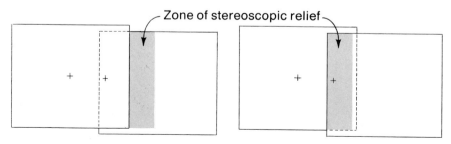

Figure 215. Viewing aerial photos stereoscopically.

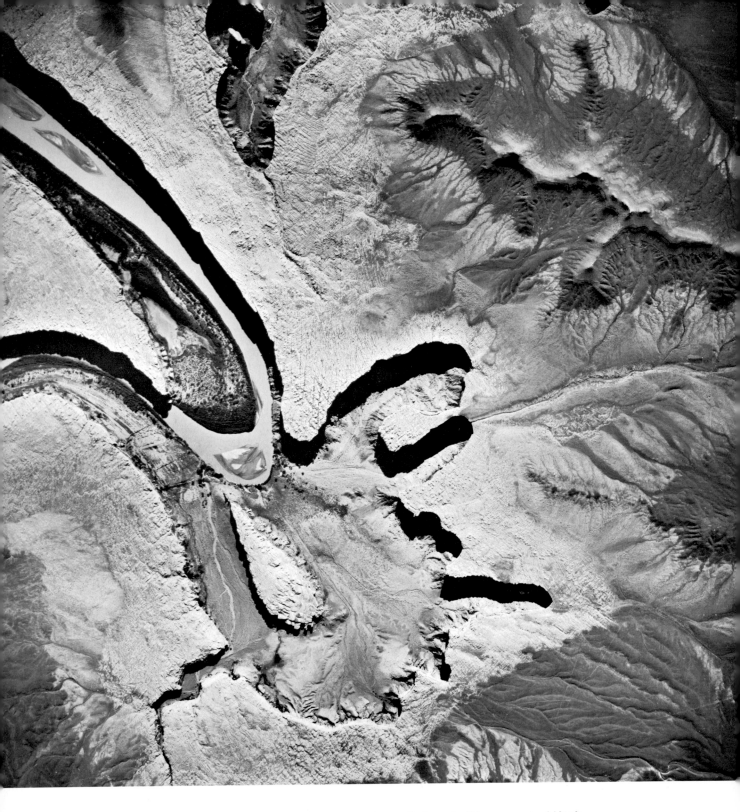

Figure 216 (left). Stream erosion—Colorado River, central Utah.

Regional uplift may cause rejuvenation of a drainage system. Various features developed during earlier stages of erosion can be seen in the present landscape.

Figure 216 (right).

0   .5   1 mile

Problems

1. What erosional features shown in the area of stereo vision were inherited from a previous stage of stream erosion?

2. How have those features been changed by the present conditions of stream erosion?

3. What material would you expect to find in the bottom of the large meander bend?

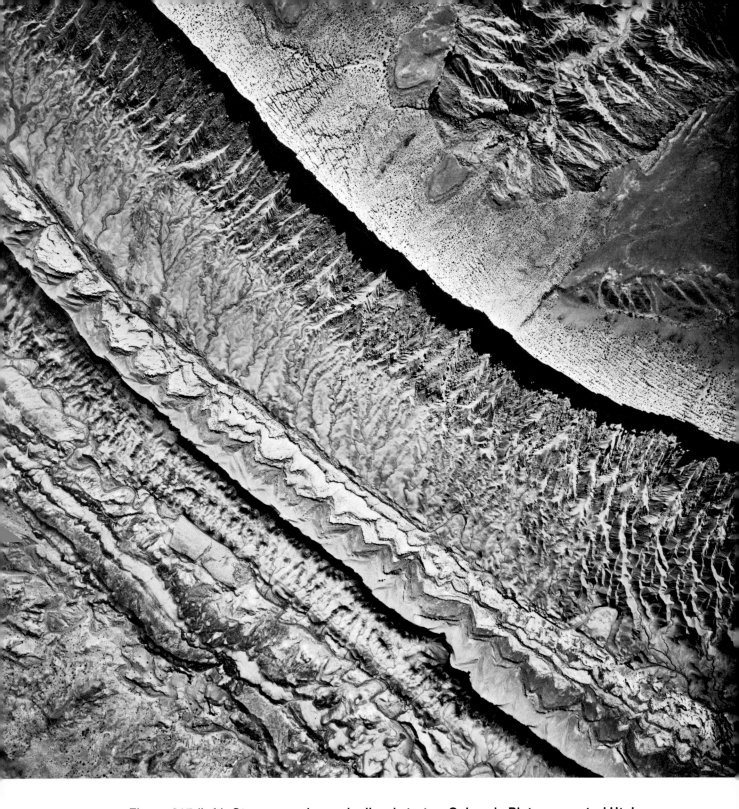

Figure 217 (left). Stream erosion on inclined strata—Colorado Plateau, central Utah.

A sequence of tilted sedimentary rocks commonly exposes formations which become eroded in a variety of ways. In arid regions sandstone and limestone are usually hard and resistant, whereas shale is weak and easily eroded.

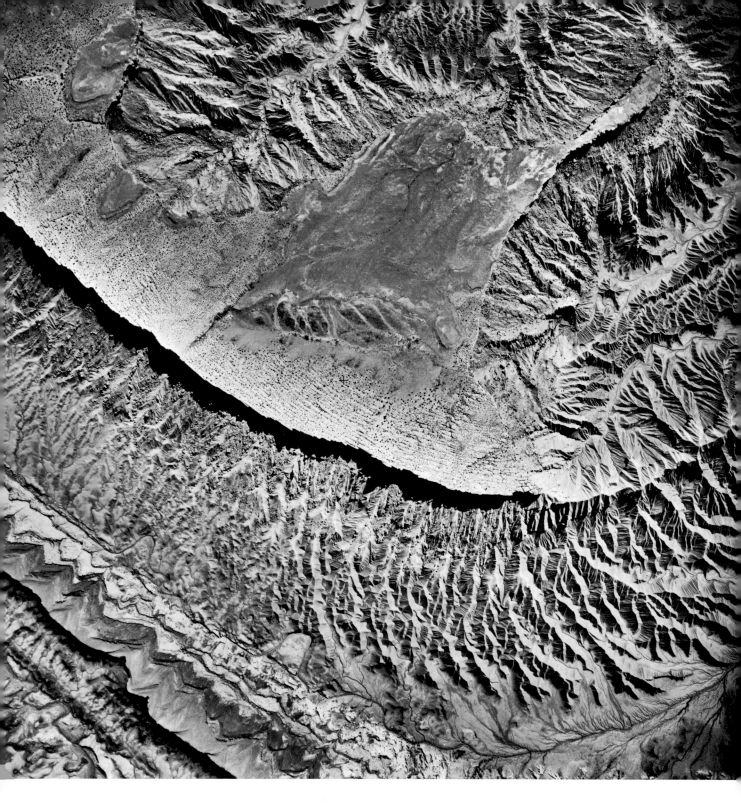

Figure 217 (right).

0 ⊦—⊦—⊦—⊦—⊦—⊦ .5 mile

Problems

1. What type of rock would tend to develop the most intricate system of tributaries?

2. Make a sketch map showing how the plateau will appear in the future.

3. Make a geologic map of the area. Show dip and strike symbols for the major formations and for the major joint systems.

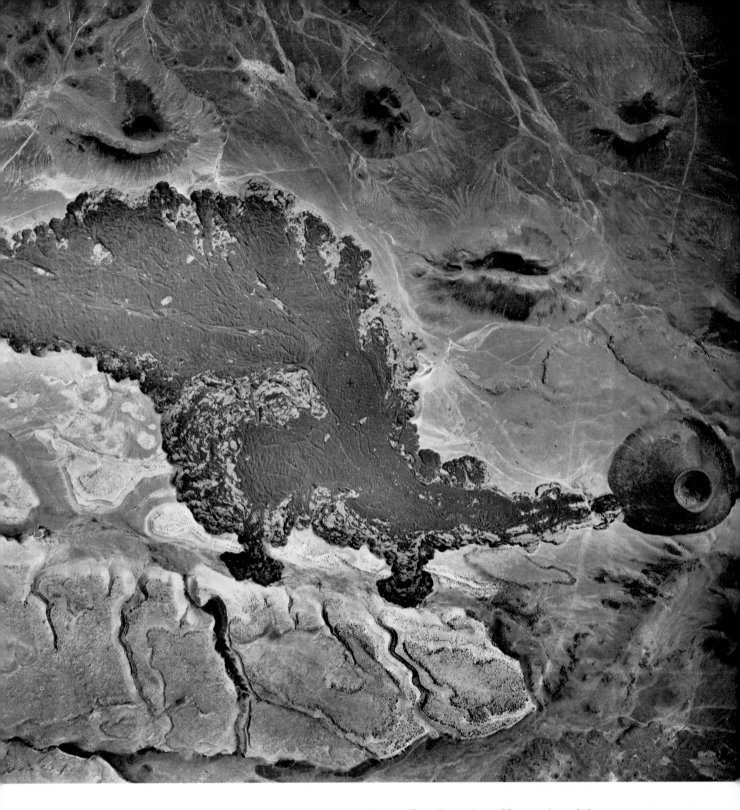

Figure 218 (left). Recent volcanic activity—San Francisco Mountains, Arizona.

As soon as volcanic material is extruded onto the surface, it is subjected to processes of erosion. Consequent streams develop on cinder cones and in a relatively short time will greatly modify or obliterate them. Streams also dissect the lava flow and establish new drainage channels along the flow margins.

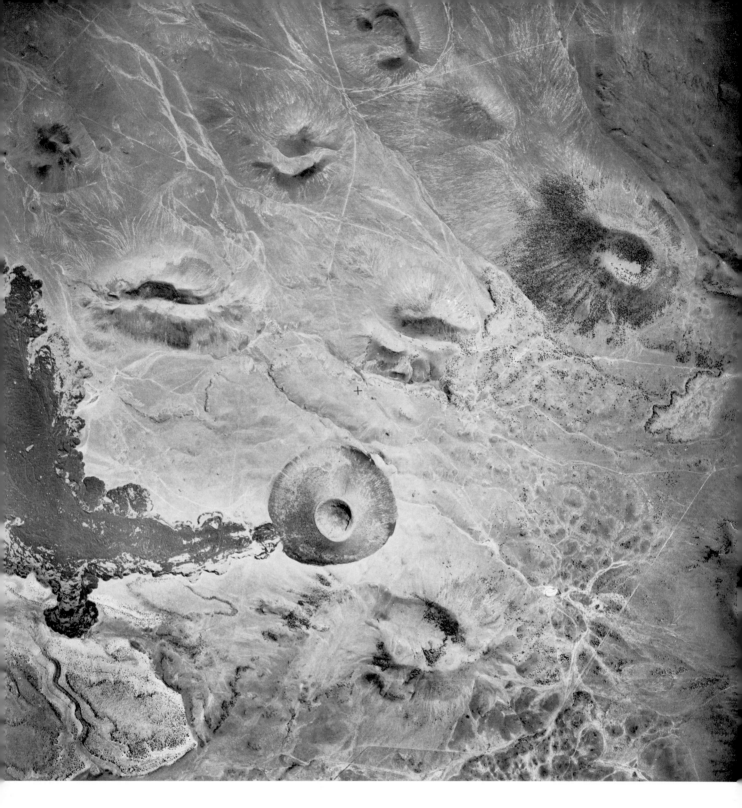

Figure 218 (right).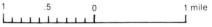

Problems

1. Study the cinder cones in this area and indicate their relative age by number (1 oldest, 2 next oldest, etc.)

2. Map the extent of the lava flow associated with the cone just south of the youngest extrusion. How have its margins and surface been modified with time?

Figure 219 (left). Marine erosion—coast of central Oregon.

Many details of coastal landforms are best seen from ground level, but regional relationships are best seen on aerial photographs.

Figure 219 (right).

0   .5 mile

Problems

1. What is the origin of the small islands in this area?

2. How do the islands affect the distribution of wave energy?

3. What evidence indicates that sea level was once higher relative to the present shoreline?

4. How will this coast be modified in the future?

Figure 220 (left). Valley glaciation—Rocky Mountains, Alberta, Canada.

The Pleistocene glaciers greatly modified many of the high mountain ranges and developed some of the most rugged and scenic landscapes in the world.

206

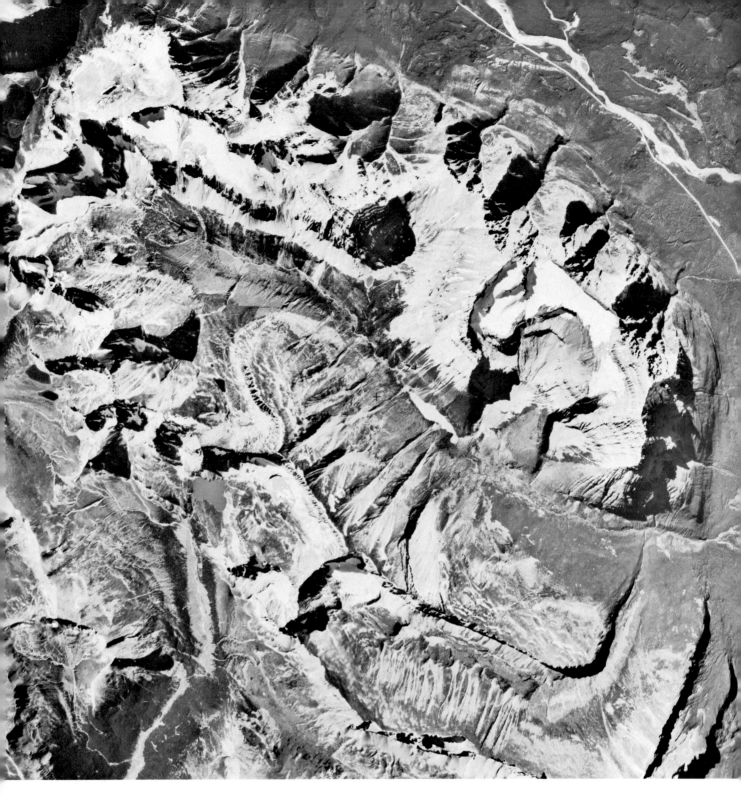

Figure 220 (right).

0 ⊢————————⊣ 1 mile

Problems

1. Identify and label all the landforms you see in stereoscopic view which were developed by glaciation.

2. Show the direction of ice flow by a series of arrows.

3. What processes of mass movement are most active in this area now?

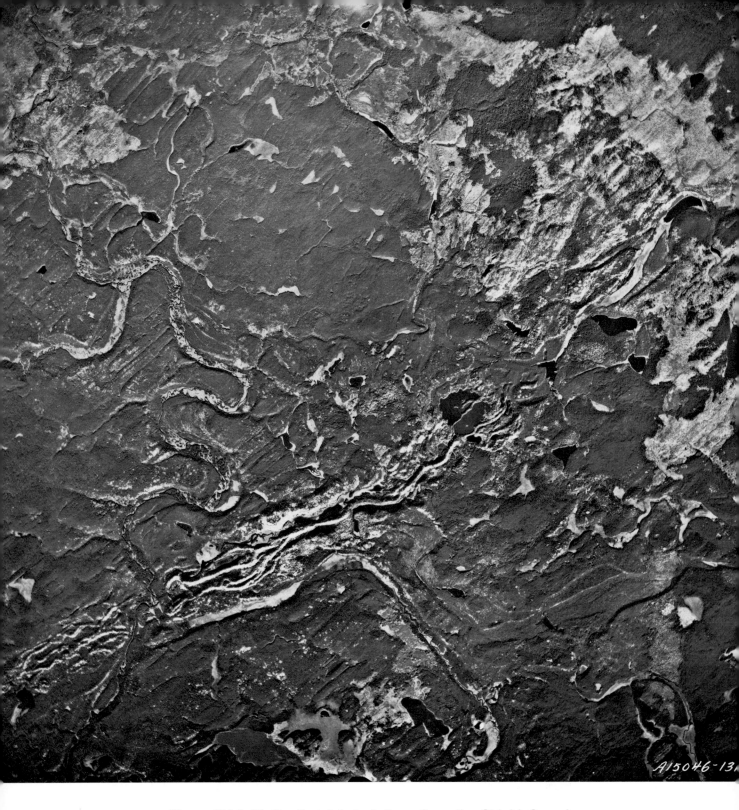

Figure 221 (left). Continental glaciation—Canadian Shield, Canada.

The Canadian Shield is a relatively flat surface that has been eroded to within a few hundred feet of sea level. As the glaciers moved across this region, they removed the topsoil and a few feet of bedrock and, in some areas, deposited the material to form a variety of landforms.

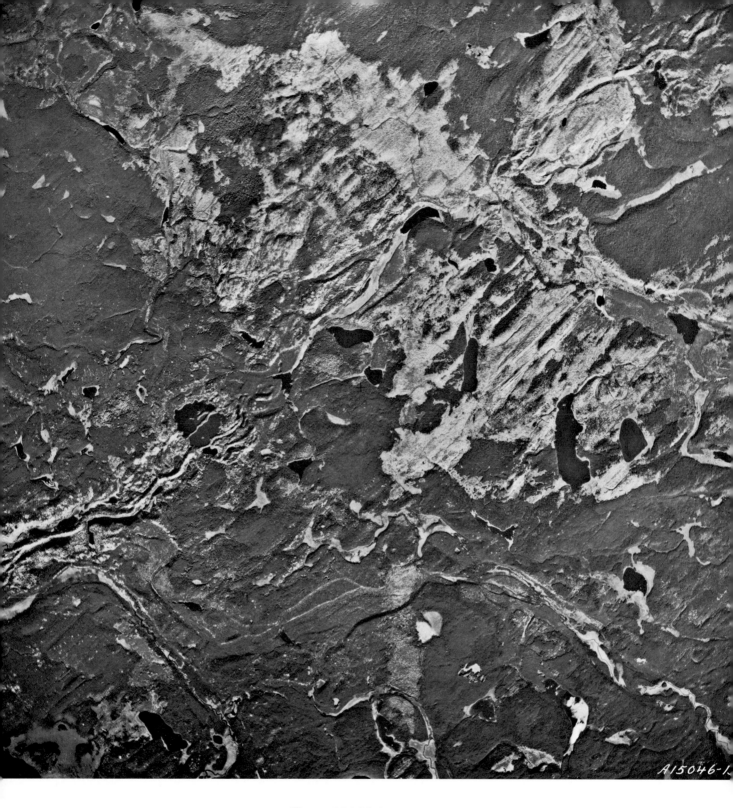

Figure 221 (right).

0 ⊢———————————⊣ 1 mile

Problems

1. Locate and label (a) eskers, (b) drumlins, (c) ancient spillways for meltwater, and (d) ground moraine.

2. Show by arrows the direction of ice movement and the direction of meltwater drainage.

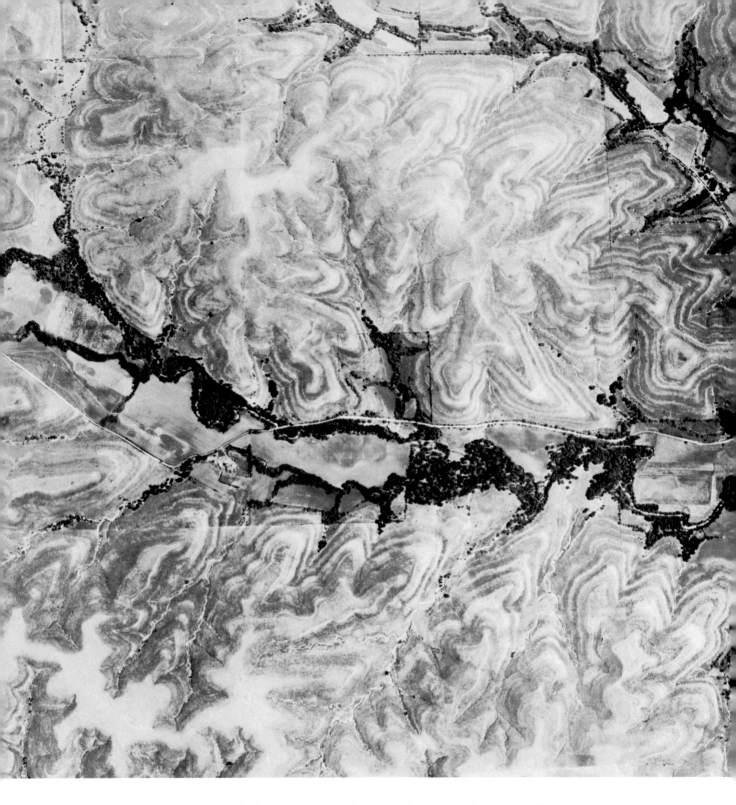

Figure 222 (left). Surface expression of horizontal rocks—Flint Hills, Kansas.

If all vegetation, soil, and cultural features could be removed from the surface of an area and the exposed rock formations painted different colors, an aerial photograph would be, in effect, a geologic map. Flint Hills approaches this situation, for many rocks are clearly expressed by variations in tone and selective growth of vegetation.

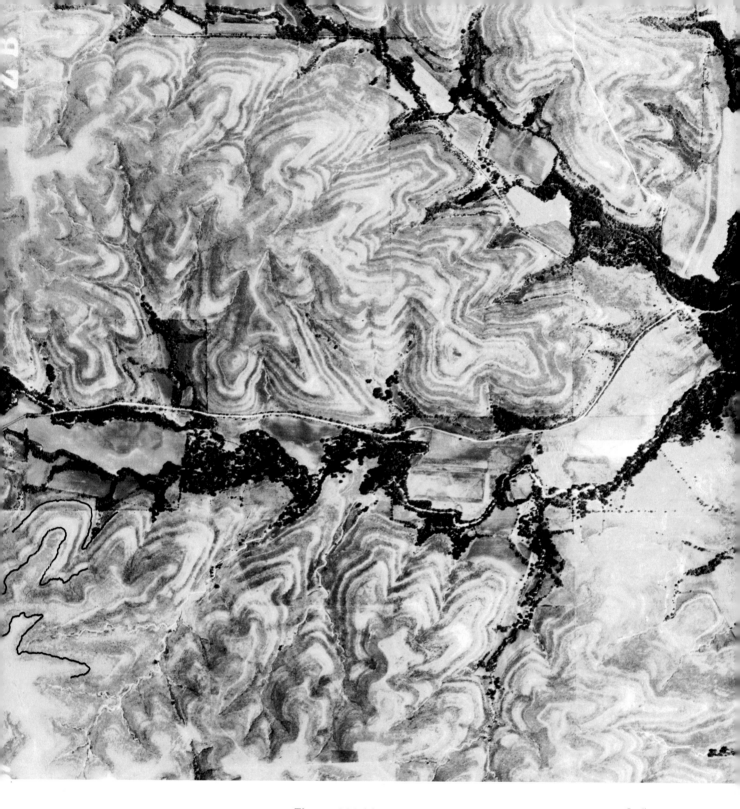

Figure 222 (right).

0 ⊢—⊢—⊢—⊢—⊢—⊣ .5 mile

Problems

1. To learn more about geologic mapping, construct a geologic map of the area shown in stereo by extending the contacts between the formations marked by black lines.

2. Number the beds according to age (1 oldest, 2 next oldest, etc.).

3. Sketch a geologic cross section across this area, showing the relationships between structure and topography.

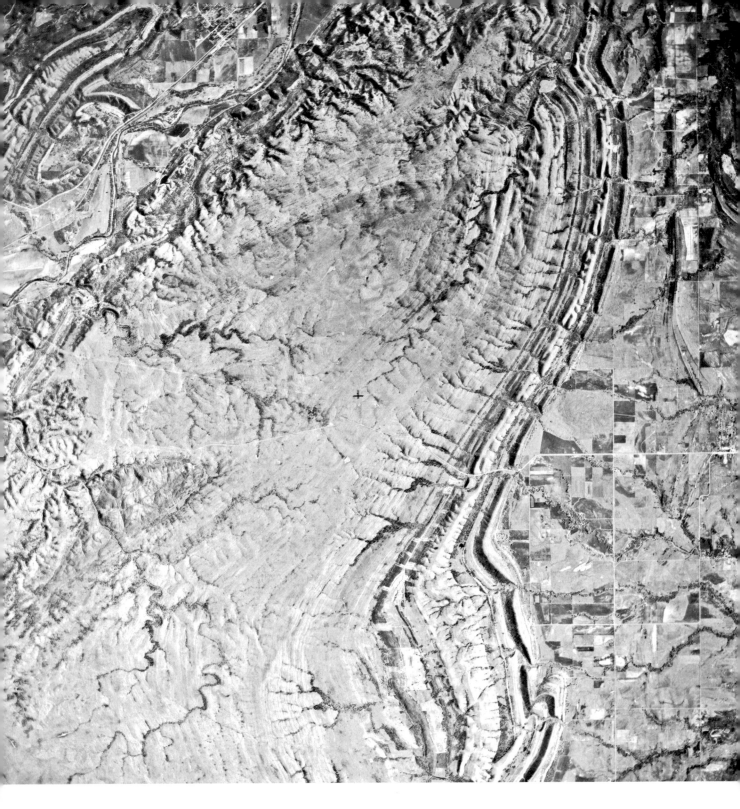

Figure 223 (left). Surface expression of inclined strata—central Oklahoma.

The bedrock in this area consists of a sequence of dipping sedimentary strata. Some formations can be traced across the entire photo, but soil partly obscures other beds.

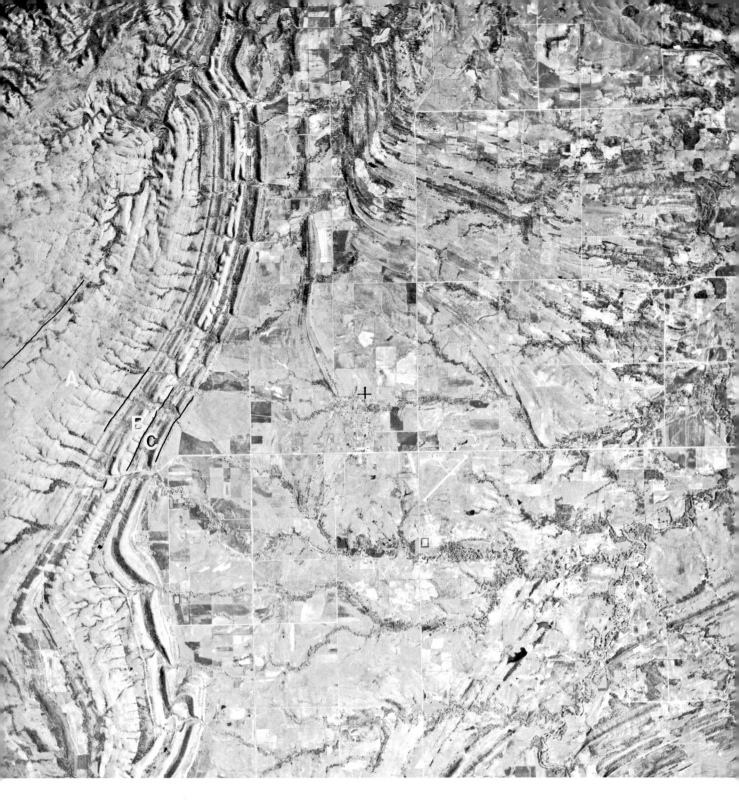

Figure 223 (right).

Scale: 1 ... .5 ... 0 ... 1 mile

Problems

1. How can you tell the direction in which the beds are dipping?

2. Estimate the angle of dip.

3. Map the rock formations labeled A, B, and C.

4. Which of these beds is thickest and which is thinnest? How did you arrive at your answers?

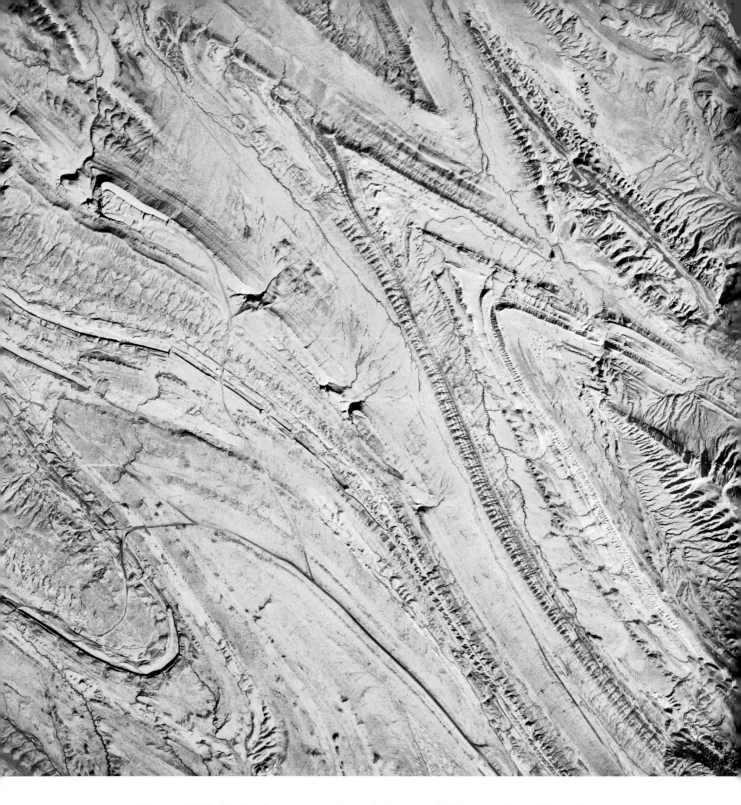

Figure 224 (left). Surface expression of plunging folds—northern Wyoming.

These stereo photographs illustrate, in fine detail, the patterns produced by erosion on folded rocks. The clarity of structural expression is enhanced by the fact that this is an arid region.

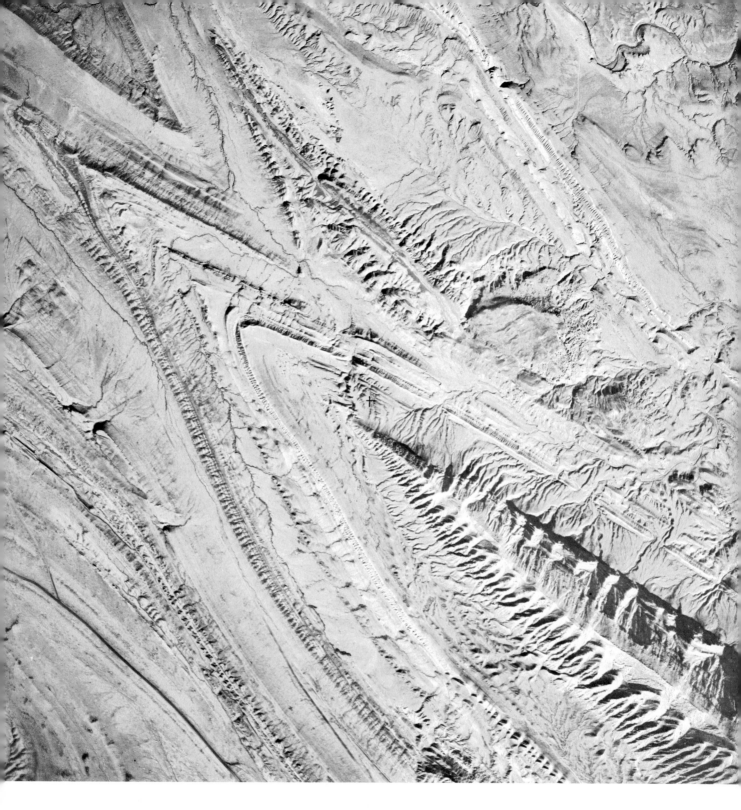

Figure 224 (right).

0   .5 mile

Problems

1. Study the strike and dip of the beds that form ridges. Draw in the geologic symbols to define the structure. Include dip and strike symbols and the axes of folds.

2. Make a geologic map of the area in stereo view by tracing the ridge-forming formations. Construct a geologic cross section from the upper right corner to the lower left corner to show the subsurface structure.

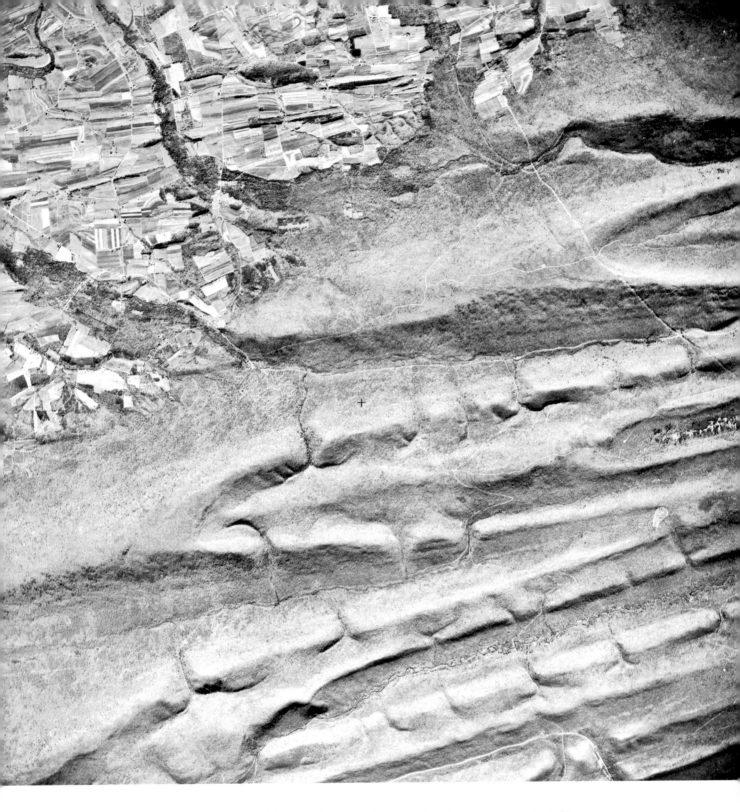

Figure 225 (left). The Valley and Ridge Province—Pennsylvania.

The Valley and Ridge Province of the Appalachian Mountains consists of a series of plunging anticlines and synclines. Resistant sandstones have been eroded into relief and form linear ridges. Shale and limestone formations are less resistant and have been eroded into long valleys.

Figure 225 (right).

Problems

1. Make a geologic map of this area by tracing out the areal extent of the major resistant sandstone units. How many units of sandstone are exposed?

2. Show the axes of all anticlines and synclines. Use the appropriate map symbols.

Figure 226 (left). Joints and normal faults—Colorado Plateau, Utah.

Thick, resistant sandstone formations in the Colorado Plateau commonly show the characteristics of fracture systems in remarkable detail. The sandstone formation in this area is nearly horizontal. Normal faults are shown where the surface is displaced vertically. Joint systems are accentuated by weathering and are expressed as cracks.

Figure 226 (right).

0   .5 mile

Problems

1. Map the normal faults in this area and label the relative movement D on the downthrown block and U on the upthrown block.

2. Compare and contrast the cliff or scarp formed by normal faulting with that produced by strike-slip faulting (see Figure 227).

3. How do the trends of the joints relate to the trends of the faults?

Figure 227 (left). Strike-slip fault—California.

The lateral displacement of strike-slip faults does not produce high scarps, but the fault line is often marked by linear ridges and valleys, structural and topographic discontinuities, and offset drainage. Recurrent movement may be expressed by small scarps that offset drainage in alluvium.

Figure 227 (right). 0 _____ .10 mile

Problems

1. Trace the fault line with red pencil. Is the fault a single plane or a zone of several parallel fault planes?

2. Study the stream pattern on both sides of the fault. How does the stream pattern show the relative movement along the fault?

3. Study the alluvium along the fault zone. How many periods of movement are expressed in the offset alluvial surfaces?

Figure 228 (left). Intrusive igneous rocks—Duncan Lake area, Northwest Territories, Canada.

Three major rock bodies are exposed in this area: (1) metamorphosed sediments (dark gray), (2) granite (light tones), and (3) basalt (long, narrow bands of dark gray tones).

Figure 228 (right).

1   .5   0   1 mile

Problems

1. What types of intrusive bodies are formed by (a) the granite and (b) the basalt?

2. Study the contacts between the granite and the basalt and determine the relative ages of these rock bodies.

3. Which rock types are most resistant to weathering? Which weather most rapidly?

Figure 229 (left). Geologic processes on the moon—Mare Imbrium.

Parts of the lunar surface have been photographed stereoscopically and can be studied in the same manner as features on the earth. The major geologic processes on the moon have been the impact of meteorites and the extrusion of lava.

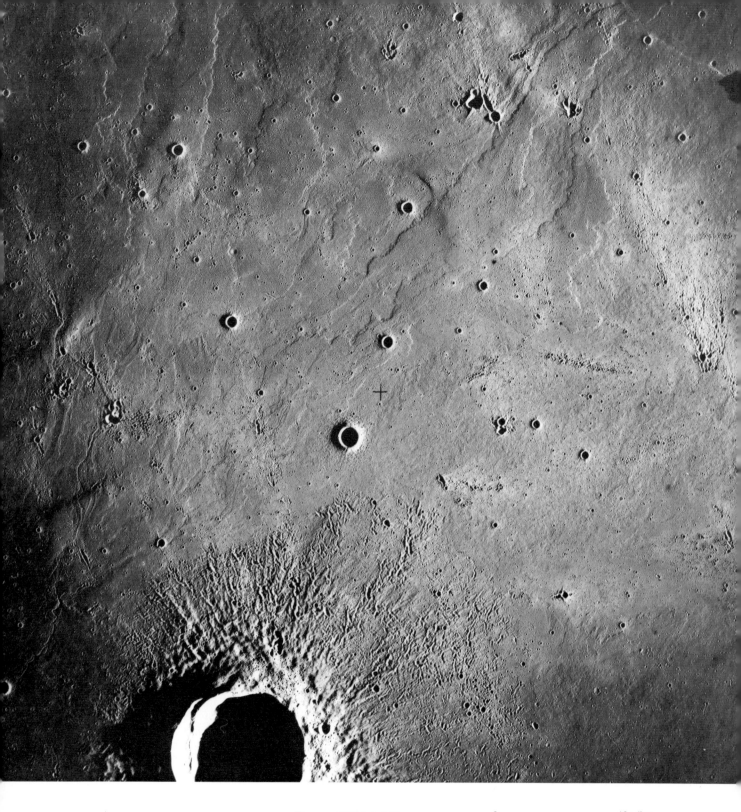

Figure 229 (right).

0   10 miles

Problems

1. Study the ejecta blanket of the large crater in the lower part of the photograph. Is this body of rock older or younger than the basalts of the surrounding maria? Explain.

2. A number of individual lava flows can be seen on this photo. Trace their margins and try to determine their relative ages. On the basis of your map, where do you think the center of the extrusion is?